STUDENT UNIT GUIDE

NEW EDITION

WJEC AS Biology Unit BY2

Biodiversity and Physiology of Body Systems

Andy Clarke

PHILIP ALLAN

This book is dedicated to my dad, who instilled in me a passion for the natural world. I would also like to thank Alex Cook for his help and advice, and my wife Blythe for her support and encouragement.

Philip Allan, an imprint of Hodder Education, an Hachette UK company, Market Place, Deddington, Oxfordshire OX15 0SE

Orders
Bookpoint Ltd, 130 Milton Park, Abingdon, Oxfordshire OX14 4SB
tel: 01235 827827
fax: 01235 400401
e-mail: education@bookpoint.co.uk
Lines are open 9.00 a.m.–5.00 p.m., Monday to Saturday, with a 24-hour message answering service. You can also order through the Philip Allan Updates website: www.philipallan.co.uk

ISBN 978-1-4441-8294-1

First printed 2013
Impression number 5 4 3 2 1
Year 2017 2016 2015 2014 2013

Cover photo: Fotolia

Typeset by Integra Software Services Pvt. Ltd., Pondicherry, India

Printed in Dubai

Hachette UK's policy is to use papers that are natural, renewable and recyclable products and made from wood grown in sustainable forests. The logging and manufacturing processes are expected to conform to the environmental regulations of the country of origin.

This material has been endorsed by WJEC and offers high quality support for the delivery of WJEC qualifications. While this material has been through a WJEC quality assurance process, all responsibility for the content remains with the publisher.

Contents

Getting the most from this book

Questions & Answers

Exam-style questions

Examiner comments on the questions
Tips on what you need to do to gain full marks, indicated by the icon ℮.

Sample student answers
Practise the questions, then look at the student answers that follow each set of questions.

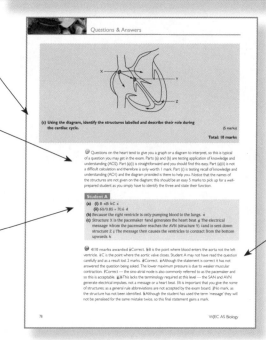

Examiner commentary on sample student answers
Find out how many marks each answer would be awarded in the exam and then read the examiner comments (preceded by the icon ℮) following each student answer. Annotations that link back to points made in the student answers show exactly how and where marks are gained or lost.

About this book

This guide will help you to prepare for BY2, the examination for WJEC AS Biology **Unit 2: Biodiversity and Physiology of Body Systems**. Your understanding of some of the principles in Unit 1 may be re-examined here as well.

The **Content Guidance** section covers all the concepts you need to understand and facts you need to know for the BY2 exam. It also includes *examiner tips* and *knowledge checks* to help you prepare for BY2. There are three aspects to the unit, and this guide, that you will find useful during your revision:

1 Body systems have evolved, by a process of natural selection, from common ancestors, so there is an **evolutionary theme** running through Unit 2. It is important that you keep this in mind as you use the guide because it will help you to understand the concepts involved. This applies especially to vertebrates, as the unit focuses on the evolution of systems for gas exchange and transport, as well as reproductive strategies, as they have evolved from fish, through amphibians to reptiles, birds and mammals.

2 The unit also follows a **comparative approach**, which requires the understanding of a particular concept, for example gas exchange, and how this concept relates to adaptations such as gills in fish, lungs in mammals and a tracheal system in insects. In each topic, the concepts are presented first and then the details of the adaptations of the different organisms are explained. It is a good idea to get your mind around these key ideas before you try to learn all the associated facts.

3 The **order** in which topics appear in the guide follows the order of the specification with the exception of plant transport, which follows directly on from gas exchange in plants. The reason for this is that gas exchange and transpiration are clearly linked and there is scope for examiners to write questions on plants that incorporate both topics. Although the characteristics of animal phyla appears in the first section of the unit (Biodiversity and classification), you may find it easier to try to learn this material last as many of the characteristics relate to gas exchange, transport and reproductive strategies.

The **Questions and Answers** section will help you to:
- familiarise yourself with many of the different question styles you can expect in the unit test
- understand what the examiners mean by terms like 'describe' and 'explain'
- interpret the question material — especially any data that the examiners give you
- write concise answers to the questions that the examiners set

In every BY2 exam there will be two 'essay-type' questions worth 10 marks, of which you will be required to answer one. This section does not include examples of this type of question, but it is important that you practise them using past exam papers.

Each question in this section is attempted by two students, Student A and Student B. Their answers, along with the examiner comments, should help you to see what you need to do to score a good mark — and how you can easily not score a good mark even though you probably understand the biology.

Content Guidance

Biodiversity and classification

Key concepts you must understand

- The variety of living organisms that exist today has evolved as a result of natural selection from pre-existing species.
- Extinction is the loss of species; the majority of all known organisms are now extinct.
- Closely related species have shared characteristics that have evolved from a common ancestor via adaptive radiation — for example, the pentadactyl limb.
- Classification systems based on shared anatomy have led to mistakes due to the presence of analogous structures, which have arisen from the process of convergent evolution.
- Modern classification systems are phylogenetic, with organisms being grouped according to evolutionary relationships as well as shared characteristics.
- Modern classification methods are more accurate and employ biochemical techniques such as DNA fingerprinting.
- All organisms are given scientific names, which are internationally recognised.

Biodiversity

Biodiversity is a measure of the number of species on the planet or in a specified area. In general the greatest biodiversity is found in the tropics and decreases as one moves towards the poles. For example, coral reefs and tropical rainforests are the most diverse habitats on the planet.

Evolutionary history shows that there have been five mass extinction events, when most species became extinct; these are referred to as **bottlenecks** in biodiversity. Since these events the fossil record shows that biodiversity has increased and new species have radiated out from a common ancestor.

Natural selection brings about the evolution of new species from a common ancestor. This is known as **adaptive radiation**.

Classification

Classification systems are **hierarchical**, i.e. larger groups are sub-divided into smaller groups. Each group, or taxon, may contain a number of groups (taxa) lower in the hierarchy. Each group has features unique to that group — for example, all mammals feed their young on milk.

Table 1 The classification of humans and the grey wolf

Increase in similarity of organisms in each taxon (group)

Taxon	Human	Grey wolf
Kingdom	Animalia	Animalia
Phylum	Chordata	Chordata
Class	Mammalia	Mammalia
Order	Primata	Carnivora
Family	Hominidae	Canidae
Genus	*Homo*	*Canis*
Species	*sapiens*	*lupus*

Examiner tip

You will need to remember the names of the seven taxonomic groups and the order in which they are arranged. The use of a mnemonic can help, for example **K**ing **P**hilip **C**ame **O**ver **F**or **G**reat **S**ausages.

Table 1 shows that as organisms are classified down the hierarchy they have more characteristics in common. Both humans and wolves have a backbone and feed their young on milk. The possession of a backbone is a characteristic they share with birds, reptiles, amphibians and fish, which all belong to the **phylum** Chordata. However, feeding their young on milk is a characteristic unique to the **class** of mammals.

The biological name of an organism follows a **binomial** (two-name) system that uses the name of its **genus** and **species**. The biological name is in Latin, which is a universal language and internationally recognised, and is printed in *italics*.

A **species** is a group of organisms that have similar characteristics, and can **interbreed** to produce **fertile** offspring.

Phylogenetic classification

Biological classification of organisms is based on the *presence of shared characteristics* and on the *evolutionary relationships* between species/groups; this is known as a **phylogenetic** system. Shared characteristics include:

- morphology and the presence of **homologous structures**, for example the pentadactyl limb in vertebrates (Figure 1)
- biochemical make-up, for example **DNA fingerprinting** and amino acid sequences of common proteins are used to estimate relatedness between species

Knowledge check 1

What are the scientific names for humans and the grey wolf?

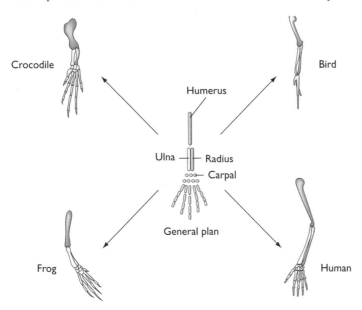

Figure 1 Pentadactyl limb

Knowledge check 2

The dorsal fin of a shark and a dolphin are evidence of common ancestry. True or false?

Analogous structures such as the wings of a bird and insect arise due to a process of **convergent evolution** and are not an indication of relatedness. Historically classification was based on morphology, but such morphological convergence led to organisms being incorrectly grouped together. **Biochemical analysis** has corrected the classification mistakes made as a result of convergent evolution.

Evolutionary relationships

The **fossil record** and **biochemical analysis** are both used to work out evolutionary relationships between organisms. Biologists generally accept that all organisms have evolved from a **common ancestor**:

- Species that have many characteristics in common are closely related and share a recent common ancestor in their evolutionary history.
- Species that have fewer characteristics in common are not closely related and share a less recent common ancestor in evolutionary history.

Figure 2 shows the evolutionary relationships between different groups of finches found on the Galapagos Islands. It demonstrates the principle of adaptive radiation and the points of divergence indicate the presence of a common ancestor between the groups.

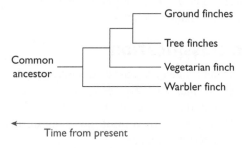

Knowledge check 3

Which two groups of finches in Figure 2 are the most closely related?

Figure 2 Evolutionary relationships between finches found on the Galapagos Islands

Summary

After studying this topic you should be able to:

- define biodiversity and understand that the variety of organisms has differed over geological time and over different parts of the world
- explain how biodiversity has been generated through natural selection and adaptation over millions of years
- use Darwin's finches on the Galapagos Islands as an example to explain adaptive radiation
- describe how organisms are classified into groups based on their evolutionary relationships

- describe how classification places organisms into discrete and hierarchical groups with other closely related species
- explain the need for classification and its tentative nature
- explain how physical features and biochemical analysis can be used to assess the relatedness of organisms
- describe how DNA/genetic fingerprinting and enzyme studies show relatedness and avoid the problem of morphological convergence
- describe the binomial system of naming organisms
- define the meaning of the term species

The variety of living organisms

Pre-existing knowledge

The basic structural and functional unit of all living organisms is the cell. Organisms are classified into one of five kingdoms based primarily on the structure of their cells. In unit one you have studied in detail the structure of animal, plant and bacterial cells; this knowledge will serve you well in answering questions based on the classification of organisms into each of their respective kingdoms.

The five kingdoms

All living organisms (except viruses) are classified into one of the following five kingdoms:

- Animalia
- Plantae
- Fungi
- Protoctista
- Prokaryotae

Animalia

Members of the Animalia are multicellular and heterotrophic. They possess a nervous system and eukaryotic cells that lack a cell wall.

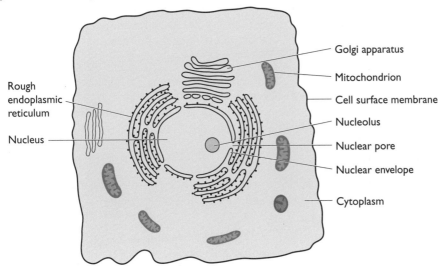

Figure 3 Animal cell

Plantae

Members of the Plantae are multicellular and autotrophic — they carry out photosynthesis. They have eukaryotic cells that have a cell wall made of cellulose, chloroplasts containing chlorophyll, and a large permanent vacuole containing cell sap.

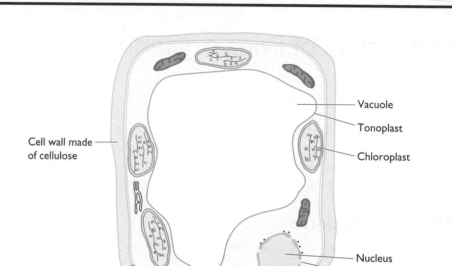

Figure 4 Plant cell

Fungi

Members of the Fungi are mainly multicellular (but can be unicellular). They have a body made of **hyphae** (network of threads) forming a **mycelium**. They are heterotrophic — either saprophytes or parasites. They possess eukaryotic cells that have a cell wall made of chitin, and reproduction is via **spores** (that lack flagella).

Protoctista

Members of the Protoctista are mostly unicellular (but can be multicellular). They possess eukaryotic cells with membrane-bound organelles present (e.g. mitochondria). They can be autotrophic or heterotrophic.

Prokaryotae

Members of the Prokaryotae are unicellular. They possess prokaryotic cells that lack membrane-bound organelles and have a cell wall made of murein. They can be autotrophic or heterotrophic.

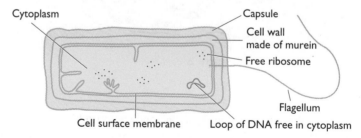

Figure 5 Prokaryotic cell

Animal phyla

In the hierarchical system the Kingdoms are sub-divided into **phyla**, which are themselves sub-divided into **classes**. Some phyla contain many more species than others and each phylum includes animals based on a shared basic body plan.

Basic characteristics of annelids

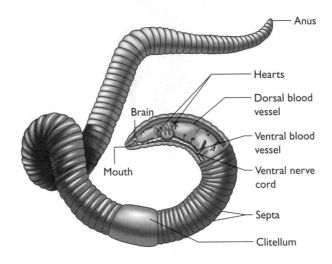

Figure 6 Earthworm

Examiner tip
The key to learning and remembering the characteristics of the different animal phyla is to think about:
- basic body plan
- how the different types of organism are adapted to:
  - gas exchange (pp.14–22)
  - transport (pp. 36–50)
  - reproduction (pp. 50–55)

This phylum includes earthworms, leeches and lugworms. Annelids have the following features:

Table 2 The basic characteristics of an annelid

Basic body plan	<ul><li>a long, thin segmented body (segments seen externally as rings)</li><li>a body divided internally by partitions (septa)</li><li>a head end with a primitive brain and a nervous system running the length of the body</li><li>a hydrostatic skeleton</li></ul>
Adaptations to gas exchange	<ul><li>a thin, permeable skin, through which gaseous exchange occurs</li></ul>
Adaptations to transport	<ul><li>a closed circulatory system, i.e. blood vessels containing an oxygen-carrying pigment, e.g. haemoglobin</li></ul>
Reproduction	<ul><li>specialised segments responsible for different functions, e.g. reproduction, excretion</li></ul>

Basic characteristics of arthropods

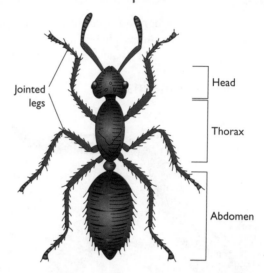

Jointed legs

Head

Thorax

Abdomen

Figure 7 Ant

Knowledge check 5

State one structural similarity between an earthworm and an ant.

Examiner tip

Although the exoskeleton provides some protection from predators, arthropods are a source of food for a wide variety of animals and are therefore heavily predated. If you are asked to state an advantage of the exoskeleton the best response you can give is to make reference to the fact that it is waterproof and prevents dehydration in terrestrial arthropods.

The arthropods are the most numerous and most successful of all the animal phyla and include millipedes, centipedes, crustaceans, spiders and insects. Arthropods have the following common features:

Table 3 The basic characteristics of an arthropod

Basic body plan	• a body divided into segments • a body further divided into head, thorax and abdomen • a hard outer exoskeleton made of chitin • pairs of jointed legs • a well-developed brain • a fluid-filled body cavity (haemocoel), which surrounds the body organs

The **exoskeleton** performs several functions:

- waterproof and therefore reduces water loss in terrestrial arthropods
- provides a point of attachment for muscles
- protects internal organs

The one main disadvantage of the exoskeleton is that it is hard and fixed in size and shape and does not grow with the animal. In order to grow an arthropod must periodically shed its exoskeleton (a process called moulting or ecdysis). As the new exoskeleton is being formed it can be stretched, resulting in a rapid increase in size of the arthropod before the exoskeleton hardens. During moulting arthropods are especially vulnerable to predation and therefore tend to hide themselves away.

Basic characteristics of insects

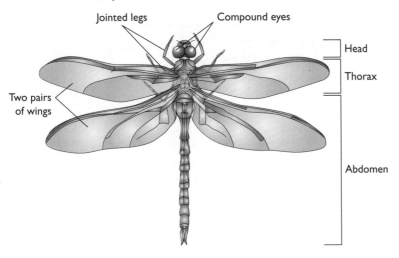

Figure 8 Dragonfly

The class Insecta is the most successful group of animals on Earth and can be used as an example of arthropod characteristics (Figure 8). 75% of all animals are insects. Insects have the following common features:

Table 4 The basic characteristics of an insect

Basic body plan	• a body divided into segments • a body further divided into head, thorax and abdomen • three pairs of jointed legs • two pairs of wings • compound eyes
Adaptations to gas exchange	• a hard outer exoskeleton made of chitin • openings on the exoskeleton called spiracles leading to a branched, chitin-lined system of tracheae • tissues supplied directly with oxygen
Adaptations to transport	• an open circulatory system lacking haemoglobin
Reproduction	• complete or incomplete metamorphosis
Other	• in the evolution of some insect groups some features may have been secondarily lost, e.g. no wings in fleas and lice

Basic characteristics of chordates

The majority of chordates possess a vertebral column (backbone) and are also known as vertebrates. They also have in common a well-developed central nervous system (CNS), including a brain enclosed within a cranium, and an internal skeleton.

The different chordate classes have the features given in Table 5.

Table 5 The basic characteristics of the five chordate classes

Fish, e.g. salmon	Amphibians, e.g. common frog	Reptiles, e.g. Nile crocodile	Birds, e.g. toucan	Mammals, e.g. spider monkey
Body covered with scales	Body covered with moist skin	Body covered with dry, waterproof scales	Body covered with feathers	Body covered with fur/hair
Gas exchange via gills	Gas exchange via skin and simple internal lungs	Gas exchange via internal lungs	Gas exchange via lungs with air sacs	Gas exchange via well-developed lungs
Single, closed circulation	'Primitive' double, closed circulation	Double, closed circulation	Double, closed circulation	Double, closed circulation
Reproduction (mainly) via external fertilisation	Reproduction via external fertilisation	Reproduction via internal fertilisation Embryo develops in amniotic egg	Reproduction via internal fertilisation Embryo develops in amniotic egg	Reproduction via internal fertilisation Embryo develops internally and receives nourishment via the placenta
Usually little or no parental care	Usually little or no parental care	Parental care shown in some species	Parental care shown in most species	High degree of parental care; young fed on milk

Summary

After studying this topic you should be able to:

- describe the basic characteristic features of the five kingdoms: Prokaryotae, Protoctista, Plantae, Fungi and Animalia
- describe the hierarchical nature of the taxa within the animal kingdom and understand that some animal phyla contain many more species than others
- explain that animals are classified into different phyla, each of which is based on a common blueprint
- describe the basic characteristics of the following phyla: annelids, arthropods and chordates
- describe the basic characteristics of the following classes: insects, fish, amphibians, reptiles, birds and mammals

Adaptations for gas exchange

Key concepts you must understand

- All living organisms exchange gases with their environment.
- Small animals exchange gases across their general body surface.
- Adaptations for gas exchange allow an increase in body size.
- Respiratory surfaces are adapted to environmental conditions.
- Large animals have specialised respiratory surfaces with common features.
- Large, active animals have ventilating mechanisms to maintain gradients across respiratory surfaces.

Living organisms exchange gases between their cells and the environment. Gas exchange occurs by **diffusion**. All gas exchange surfaces must have the following properties:

- **permeable** to gases
- **moist**, because gases must dissolve before they can diffuse across membranes

- **large surface area**
- **thin**, to provide a short diffusion pathway

Large, active animals can also have **ventilating mechanisms** to maintain steep concentration gradients across the gas exchange surface. The *rate* of diffusion of gases is increased by:
- increasing the surface area
- reducing the length of the diffusion pathway
- increasing the steepness of the concentration gradient

Knowledge check 7

State three features that are common to *all* gas exchange surfaces.

Surface area-to-volume ratio

All organisms require O_2 for cellular respiration. The *quantity* of O_2 required by an organism is proportional to its volume. The *rate of uptake* of O_2 from the environment is proportional to its surface area. Figure 9 shows the relationship between an increase in size and the surface area-to volume ratio.

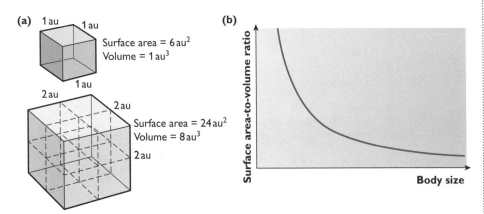

Figure 9 (a) The effect of increasing size on the surface area and volume of a cube (au = arbitrary units) (b) The relationship between size and surface area-to volume ratio

The smaller (pink) cube has a surface area-to-volume ratio of 6:1, whereas the larger (blue) cube has a surface area-to-volume ratio of only 3:1. This demonstrates that as organisms get bigger their surface area-to-volume ratio decreases. This is also shown by the curve in Figure 9(b).

A small unicellular organism, such as an amoeba, has a large surface area-to-volume ratio and short diffusion pathways to all parts of the cell.

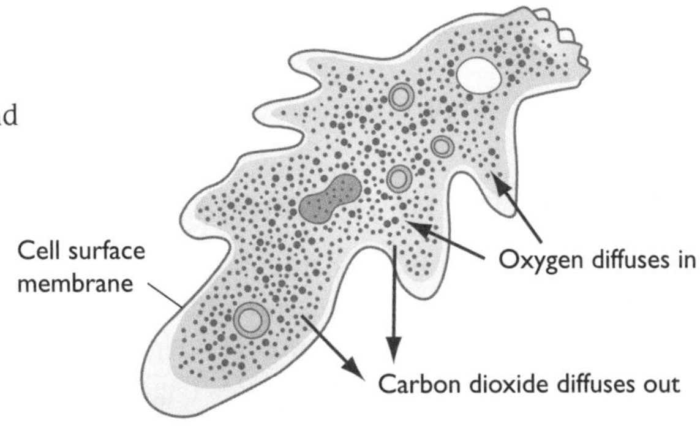

Cell surface membrane

Oxygen diffuses in

Carbon dioxide diffuses out

Figure 10 Amoeba

As organisms get larger their demand for oxygen increases but their surface area-to-volume ratio decreases. Multicellular organisms have therefore evolved adaptations to maintain adequate gas exchange to meet their increased demand for O_2. For example, the flattened body of a flatworm both increases its surface area-to-volume ratio and reduces the diffusion pathway (allowing its body surface to continue to be the gas exchange surface). Arthropods and vertebrates have evolved specialised gas exchange surfaces.

Gas exchange in mammals

Figure 11 shows the generalised structure of the human gas exchange system. The trachea, bronchi and bronchioles contain rings of cartilage, which prevent these airways from collapsing under the negative pressure produced in the lungs during inspiration.

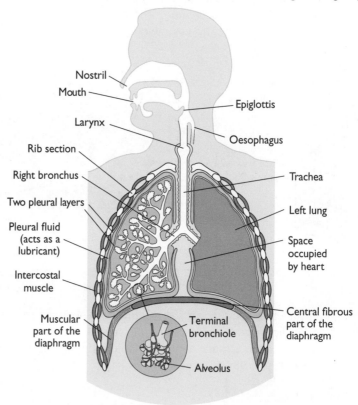

Figure 11 Structure of the human gas exchange system

Ventilation in mammals

Ventilation is the movement of the respiratory medium over the respiratory surface.

Ventilation in mammals is brought about by changing the pressure inside the lungs; air always moves down a pressure gradient. Inspiration is an active process brought about by the contraction of muscles (Figure 12(a)). Expiration is a passive process caused by the recoil of elastic tissues (Figure 12(b)).

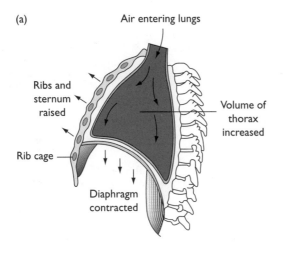

(a)

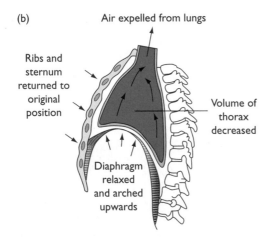

(b)

Figure 12 Mechanism of breathing showing (a) inspiration and (b) expiration

Table 6 summarises the events that occur during inspiration and expiration in a mammal.

Table 6

	Inspiration	Expiration
Intercostal muscles	Contract	Relax
Rib cage	Moves upwards and outwards	Moves downwards and inwards
Diaphragm muscles	Contract	Relax
Diaphragm	Flattened	Dome shaped
Volume of thoracic cavity	Increases	Decreases
Pressure in thoracic cavity and lungs	Decreases (below atmospheric pressure)	Increases (above atmospheric pressure)
Direction of air flow	Into the lungs	Out of the lungs

Gas exchange takes place in the alveoli. Figure 13 shows the structure and associated gas exchange pathways of an alveolus and associated capillary. Table 7 shows how the lungs are adapted for gas exchange.

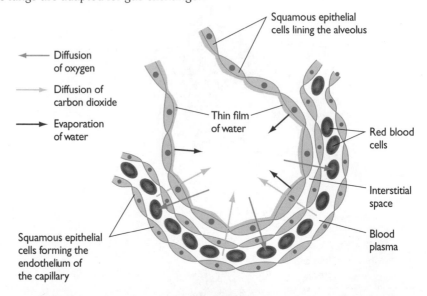

Figure 13 Gas exchange between an alveolus and a blood capillary

Table 7 The adaptations shown by mammalian lungs for gas exchange

Feature	Adaptations
Moist surface	• Tissue fluid lining the alveolus allows gases to dissolve and diffuse across
Large surface area	• Millions of alveoli • An extensive capillary network surrounding each alveolus
Short diffusion pathway	• The alveolar wall is a single layer of flattened epithelial cells • The capillary wall is a single layer of flattened endothelial cells
Maintenance of steep concentration gradients	• Ventilation ensures the O_2 concentration in the alveolus is high • A dense capillary network and blood flow ensure that the O_2 concentration entering the alveolar capillaries is low

Gas exchange in other terrestrial animals

Air is the respiratory medium used by terrestrial animals. As gas exchange surfaces must be moist terrestrial animals face dehydration due to water evaporating from respiratory surfaces.

Annelids (e.g. earthworm)

- They use their body surface for gas exchange.
- They secrete mucus to ensure their 'skin' remains moist.
- They are elongated — providing a large surface area-to-volume ratio.
- Their capillary network is well developed and close to the surface — providing a short diffusion pathway.
- Their blood contains haemoglobin with a high affinity for oxygen.

Insects

Insects have a waterproof exoskeleton made of **chitin**. Openings on the exoskeleton called **spiracles** lead to a branched, chitin-lined system of **tracheae**. The gas exchange surfaces are the **tracheoles**, which come into contact with every tissue. The advantages of this system are that every tissue is supplied directly with oxygen and no circulation or haemoglobin is needed.

Large insects contract and relax muscles in their thorax and abdomen, causing rhythmical movements that ventilate the tracheoles, maintaining a concentration gradient.

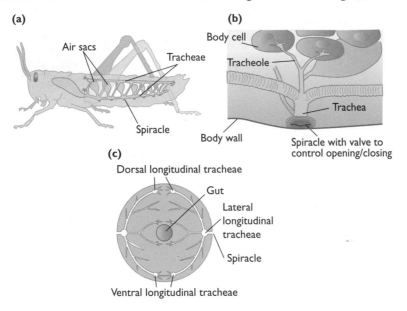

Figure 14 (a) The tracheal system of an insect (b) The relationship between spiracles, tracheae and tracheoles (c) Transverse section of the insect tracheal system

Vertebrates

Vertebrates are large animals and therefore the surface area of their skin is insufficient to act as a gas exchange surface. Terrestrial vertebrates have therefore evolved **internal lungs** for gas exchange. These provide a large surface area and minimise water loss as they are within the body cavity.

Amphibians (e.g. frog)

- The larval form (tadpole) uses gills.
- The frog's lungs are a pair of thin-walled sacs.
- As adults the inactive frog uses its moist skin for gas exchange but when active uses its lungs for gas exchange.

Reptiles

- Reptile lungs are more efficient than amphibian lungs as they more highly folded, giving them a much greater surface area.
- Reptiles also have a ribcage and can therefore ventilate their lungs.

Birds

- Although the ventilation of bird lungs is similar to that of reptiles, its effectiveness is increased by the presence of air sacs.
- Although no gas exchange occurs in the air sacs, their arrangement increases the efficiency of lung ventilation by acting as bellows.

Gas exchange in fish

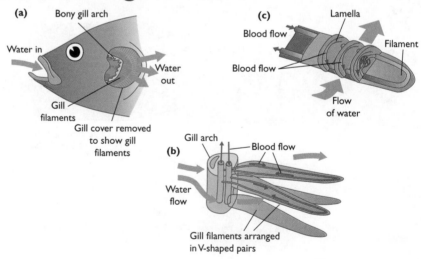

Figure 15 (a) The position of gills (b) The structure of gill filaments (c) Blood flow in lamellae

Water is the respiratory medium used by fish. It is a dense medium, and passes over the gill lamellae in a **unidirectional flow**. Fish have evolved gills, with **gill lamellae** which are adapted to gas exchange in the ways shown in Table 8.

Table 8 The adaptations shown by gill lamellae for gas exchange

Feature	Adaptations
Large surface area	• Millions of gill lamellae
Short diffusion pathway	• Gill lamellae are thin
Maintenance of steep concentration gradients	• Ventilation (oxygenated water is forced over the gills) ensures the O_2 concentration of the water entering the gills is relatively high. • Dense capillary network and blood flow ensure that oxygenated blood is removed from the lamellae and replaced with deoxygenated blood with a low O_2 concentration. • Blood contains haemoglobin with a high affinity for oxygen.

Countercurrent mechanism

The concentration of (dissolved) oxygen in water is much lower than in air and therefore bony fish have evolved an efficient mechanism of gas exchange. Water flows over the gills in the opposite direction from that of the blood in the gill lamellae — this is known as a **countercurrent flow** (see Figures 15(c) and 16).

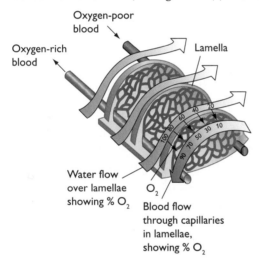

Figure 16 A single gill lamella

The countercurrent mechanism makes gas exchange very efficient because the concentration of O_2 in the water is always higher than the concentration of O_2 in the blood, i.e. equilibrium is never reached (see Figure 17). This enables O_2 to diffuse into blood along the *whole length* of the gill lamellae. This mechanism allows bony fish, such as herring, to extract about 80% of oxygen in water.

In cartilaginous fish (sharks and rays), such as the dogfish, water flows over the gills in the same direction as that of the blood in the gill lamellae — this is known as **parallel flow**. This is a less efficient mechanism for gas exchange because the concentration of O_2 in the water and the blood reaches equilibrium part way across the gill lamellae. As a result the dogfish can extract only about 50% of the oxygen in water.

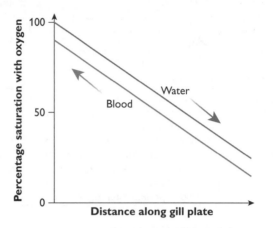

Figure 17 Oxygen concentration in water and blood

Knowledge check 11

Name the gas exchange surface found in each of the following organisms: amoeba, earthworm, insect, fish and mammal.

Gas exchange in plants

Plants require CO_2, as well as light, for photosynthesis. Their leaves are adapted for both light absorption and gas exchange. Plants rely entirely on **diffusion** for the exchange of gases.

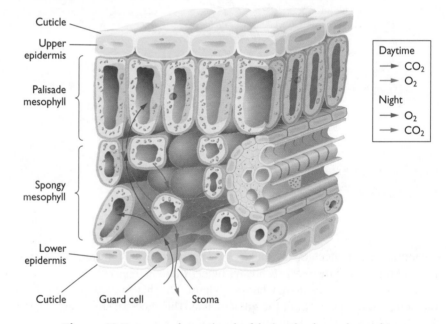

Figure 18 Net gas exchange in a leaf during the day and at night

Adaptations for light absorption

- Plants can orientate their leaves towards the light to expose a greater surface area.
- Leaves are flat and have a large surface area to absorb maximum light.
- Leaves are thin to allow light to penetrate to lower tissue layers.

- The cuticle and epidermis are transparent to allow light to penetrate mesophyll tissue.
- Palisade cells are elongated to reduce the total number of cell walls that would absorb light (preventing it reaching the chloroplasts).
- Palisade cells contain many **chloroplasts** to maximise light absorption.
- Chloroplasts move inside cells to gain the best position for absorbing light.

Adaptations for gas exchange/CO_2 absorption

- Leaves are thin to reduce the diffusion distance.
- The **spongy mesophyll**:
    - has a large surface area for gas exchange
    - contains air spaces to allow the circulation of gases and reduce the diffusion pathway of CO_2 into cells
    - is moist, for the absorption of CO_2
- **Stomatal pores** allow the entry of gases into the air spaces.

Adaptations to reduce water loss

Plants face the same problems as terrestrial animals — in order for gas exchange to occur gas exchange surfaces must be moist. However, as a consequence, water evaporates from the gas exchange surface and dehydrates the organism. Plants (like animals) cannot prevent water loss but they have adaptations to reduce it:

- Leaves have a **waxy cuticle** on the **upper epidermis** to reduce water loss by evaporation (however, this prevents gaseous exchange).
- The majority of water loss from a plant is via the stomatal pores.
- The stomatal pores are located on the **lower epidermis**, which helps to reduce water loss via evaporation.
- **Guard cells** surrounding the stomata can change shape:
    - they open the stomatal pores during the day to allow gas exchange
    - they close the stomatal pores at night to reduce water loss

Mechanism of stomatal opening

Guard cells are the only cells in the lower epidermis to contain chloroplasts. During the day (when light is available) photosynthesis occurs, which results in:

- increased production of **ATP**
- a lower CO_2 concentration in the guard cells

The ATP is used to **actively transport** K^+ into the guard cells (from the epidermal cells). The lower CO_2 concentration triggers the conversion of insoluble starch to soluble malate. The K^+ and the malate lower the **water potential** in the guard cells. Water moves into the guard cells via osmosis. This causes the guard cells to swell and become **turgid**. The inner cell wall is thicker (and less elastic) than the outer cell wall, so as the cells swell they curve apart — opening the stomatal pore (as shown in Figure 19).

Knowledge check 12

Explain why it would be a disadvantage to the plant if the stomata remained open permanently.

Examiner tip

Many students confuse the stomatal pore with the guard cells and refer to water moving into the stomata by osmosis. Some also fail to appreciate that guard cells function in pairs and as they curve apart from each other the stomatal pore opens.

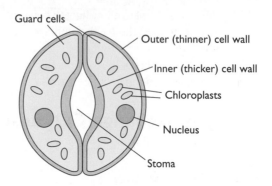

Figure 19 Guard cells

Summary

After studying this topic you should be able to:

- describe the common features of efficient gas exchange surfaces
- explain why small animals exchange gases across their general body surface
- compare gas exchange in amoeba, flatworms and earthworms
- use your understanding of surface area-to-volume ratio to explain why adaptations for gas exchange allow for an increase in body size
- explain how respiratory surfaces are adapted to environmental conditions — gills for aquatic environments, lungs for terrestrial environments
- use your knowledge of the common features of gas exchange surfaces to describe the adaptations of the specialised respiratory systems of larger terrestrial animals

- explain why large, active animals have ventilating mechanisms to maintain gradients across respiratory surfaces
- describe and explain the importance of countercurrent flow in bony fish
- describe the structure and function of the human breathing system
- describe the processes of ventilation and gas exchange in humans
- describe the features of the insect tracheal system and explain why it is a good example of adaptation to life on dry land
- describe the structure of the angiosperm leaf
- explain why the features of the leaf allow it to function as an organ of gas exchange
- explain the role of leaf structures in allowing the plant to function and photosynthesise effectively
- describe and explain the process of stomatal opening and closing

Transport in plants

Key concepts you must understand

- Plants are large, multicellular organisms and have well-developed vascular tissue to allow the transport of water, mineral ions and organic solutes.
- Water and mineral ions are transported from the roots to the leaves of plants in the xylem.
- Organic solutes, such as sucrose, are transported from the leaves to other parts of the plant in the phloem.
- There is evidence to support different theories to explain how water, mineral ions and organic solutes are transported in plants.
- The use of autoradiography can provide evidence to support theories for the movement of organic solutes.

Pre-existing knowledge

The uptake of mineral ions from the soil involves active transport, which you studied in detail in Unit 1. Remember that active transport requires specific carrier proteins in the plasma membrane and the use of ATP (produced during respiration in mitochondria) to transport ions against a concentration gradient.

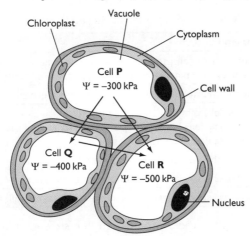

Figure 20 Water movement (indicated by arrows) between three mesophyll cells in a leaf; Cell P has the highest water potential and the water potential of Cell Q is higher than that of Cell R

The movement of water involves osmosis, which you also studied in Unit 1:
- Osmosis is the movement of water down a water potential gradient through a selectively permeable membrane.
- The water potential of a cell can be lowered by increasing the concentration of solutes, such as mineral ions, in the cytoplasm.

In order to photosynthesise, the stomatal pores on a leaf must be open to allow gas exchange. However, this results in water loss from the plant and is linked to the movement of water through the xylem.

Plant anatomy

Transverse section of the dicotyledon root

Figure 21 shows the distribution of xylem and phloem tissue in a root and stem of a dicotyledonous plant.

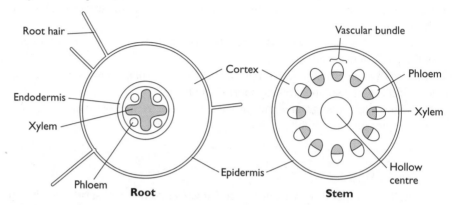

Figure 21 The distribution of xylem and phloem in cross-sections of a root and a stem

Table 9 shows the function of the different tissues in a root.

Table 9 The function of the different tissues in a root.

Structure	Function
Epidermis	Outer layer of cells, some of which are specialised into **root hair cells** — these provide an increased surface area for the uptake of ions and water
Root cortex	Made of **parenchyma** cells, which provide mechanical support to the root
Endodermis	Layer of cells that surround the pericycle Endodermal cells have a **Casparian strip** around them which is made of **suberin** (a waxy substance) that waterproofs the cell walls
Pericycle	Contains the **vascular tissue** (xylem and phloem).
Xylem	Transports water and mineral ion within the plant
Phloem	Transports sucrose (and other organic solutes) within the plant

Figure 22 is a photograph of the central region (the stele) of a dicotyledonous root, showing the distribution of xylem and phloem tissue as well as the endodermis.

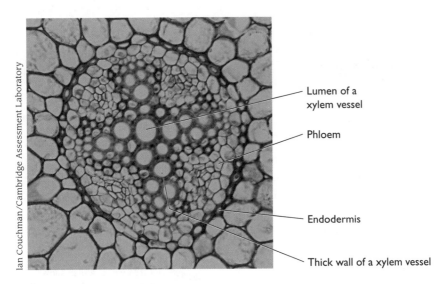

Ian Couchman/Cambridge Assessment Laboratory

Lumen of a
xylem vessel

Phloem

Endodermis

Thick wall of a xylem vessel

Figure 22 Photograph of the central region (the stele) of a dicotyledonous root

The distribution of xylem and phloem in the stem is different from that in the root (see Figure 21 and Figure 23). The stem contains discrete **vascular bundles** located towards the periphery. The phloem is located on the outer part of the vascular bundle and the xylem on the inner part.

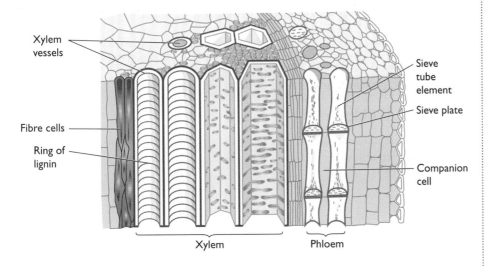

Xylem
vessels

Fibre cells

Ring of
lignin

Xylem

Phloem

Sieve
tube
element

Sieve plate

Companion
cell

Figure 23 Transport pathways in a plant system; xylem vessels and phloem sieve tubes in longitudinal and transverse sections

Vascular tissue

Structure of xylem

Xylem tissue is made up of four types of cell:

- vessels (elements)
- tracheids
- fibres
- parenchyma

Vessels and **tracheids** are composed of dead, elongated cells with pits in them (see Figure 24). Vessels are long, tubular structures formed by the end-to end fusion of vessel elements and the breakdown of their end walls. Their walls are waterproofed and strengthened by **lignin**. The function of vessels and tracheids is to transport water and mineral ions.

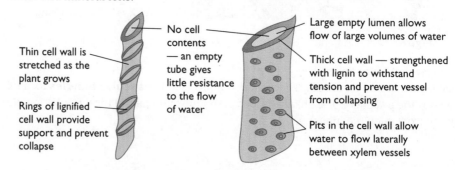

Figure 24 Two xylem vessel elements: (a) a narrow vessel thickened with rings; (b) a wider vessel with pits to allow lateral movement of water

The **fibres** and **parenchyma** provide support to the tissue.

Structure of phloem

Phloem tissue is made up of four types of cell:

- sieve tube elements
- companion cells
- fibres
- parenchyma

Sieve tubes are formed by the end-to-end fusion of **sieve tube elements**. They lack a nucleus, and the cytoplasm forms a thin layer around the periphery of the cell. The cell walls at the ends of each cell are perforated to form **sieve plates**, which allow the cytoplasm from one cell to run into adjacent cells. Their function is to transport organic solutes, e.g. sucrose and amino acids.

Companion cells lie next to sieve tubes and are linked to them via **plasmodesmata**. Companion cells contain many cell organelles, especially **mitochondria**, and are involved in loading and unloading of the sieve tubes with solutes.

Figure 25 shows the structures of the sieve tube elements and the companion cells — note the sieve pores and the plasmodesmata, which adapt these cells to their specific functions.

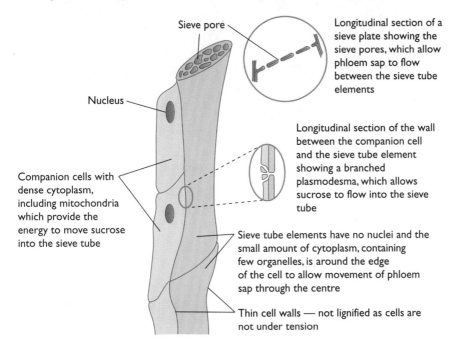

Sieve pore

Longitudinal section of a sieve plate showing the sieve pores, which allow phloem sap to flow between the sieve tube elements

Nucleus

Longitudinal section of the wall between the companion cell and the sieve tube element showing a branched plasmodesma, which allows sucrose to flow into the sieve tube

Companion cells with dense cytoplasm, including mitochondria which provide the energy to move sucrose into the sieve tube

Sieve tube elements have no nuclei and the small amount of cytoplasm, containing few organelles, is around the edge of the cell to allow movement of phloem sap through the centre

Thin cell walls — not lignified as cells are not under tension

Figure 25 Phloem sieve tubes and companion cells

Knowledge check 13

The conducting cells of xylem (vessels and tracheids) are dead when mature, yet the conducting cells of phloem (sieve tube elements) are alive. Explain the reason for this difference.

The fibres and parenchyma provide support to the tissue.

Uptake and movement of water and minerals in the root

Most absorption of water is through the **root hairs**, which provide a large surface area. Ions are absorbed by **diffusion** and **active transport**, while water is absorbed by **osmosis** from a higher potential in the soil water to a lower potential in the xylem.

Water and mineral ions move through the root by three pathways (Figure 26):
- **apoplast pathway** — through the cell walls and the spaces between cells
- **symplast pathway** — through the cytoplasm via plasmodesmata
- **vacuolar pathway** — from vacuole to vacuole in adjacent cells

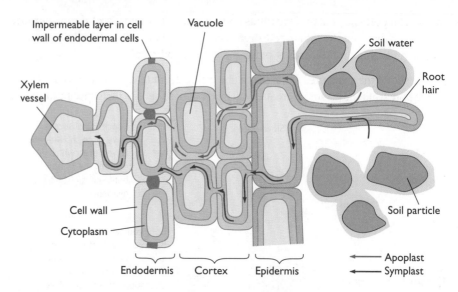

Figure 26 The pathways taken by water as it moves from the soil, into a root hair, across the cortex, through the endodermis and into the xylem; plasmodesmata are shown as the green shaded areas passing through the cell walls, but they are not as big as shown here

The endodermis

Suberin (a waterproof substance) is deposited in the cell walls and forms bands called **Casparian strips** in the endodermal cells, which block the apoplast pathway. Mineral ions are actively transported into the cytoplasm of the cells (symplast pathway). This lowers the water potential of the cells, causing water to move into the symplast pathway by osmosis.

The endodermal cells actively pump ions into the xylem — this helps to generate a water potential gradient across the root, drawing water in from the soil. The endodermis allows the plant to selectively uptake ions from the soil.

Movement of water through the stem

There are three possible theories that explain the movement of water up the xylem:
- root pressure theory
- cohesion–tension theory
- capillarity/adhesion theory

Root pressure theory

Endodermal cells actively transport ions into the xylem vessels. This lowers the water potential so water enters the xylem by osmosis creating **hydrostatic pressure** (root pressure). This root pressure forces water up the stem, but it is not sufficient to push water to the leaves at the top of tall plants.

Knowledge check 14

What is the difference between the apoplast and symplast pathways, and which one is blocked at the endodermis?

Examiner tip

If plant roots are treated with a respiratory poison, e.g. cyanide, then the uptake of minerals will stop as no ATP is generated.

Cohesion–tension theory

Transpiration is the loss of water vapour from plant leaves. Water evaporates from the spongy mesophyll cells into the air spaces and diffuses out of the stomata down a water potential gradient. This sets up a water potential gradient across the leaf from a higher potential in the xylem to a lower potential in the air spaces.

As water is drawn out of the xylem it creates **tension** on the water molecules. Water molecules show **cohesion** — they are bonded together by weak hydrogen bonds. In this way transpiration from the leaves pulls water up the stem in a continuous column called the **transpiration stream**.

Figure 27 shows the events that take place during transpiration.

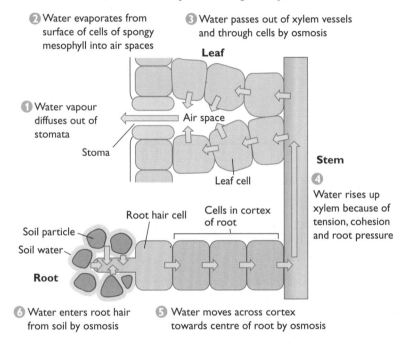

Figure 27 Transpiration — the movement of water through a plant

Capillarity/adhesion theory

Xylem vessels are narrow and have a hydrophilic lining. Water molecules are strongly attracted and **adhere** to the hydrophilic walls, causing water to move up the vessel by capillarity.

Examiner tip
Cohesion–tension theory is the only theory that can explain how water can reach the leaves of tall plants such as trees. It is therefore important that you know this theory in detail, as this will allow you to pick up the majority of the marks available on questions on transport of water up a stem.

Measuring transpiration rate

Different environmental factors can affect the rate of transpiration, and these can be investigated using a **potometer** (Figure 28).

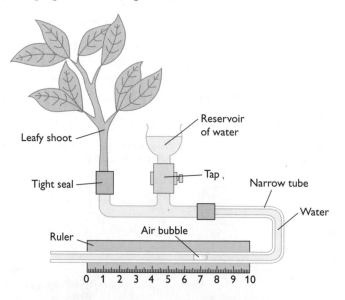

Figure 28 A typical school or college potometer for measuring the rate of water uptake by leafy shoots

Examiner tip

To obtain accurate results it is important that the water in the xylem vessels is continuous with the water in the potometer. This is why the shoot is cut underwater and attached to the potometer with an air-tight seal.

To set up the investigation a leafy shoot is cut underwater and placed into the bung of the potometer, which is filled with water. The shoot should then be left for 5 minutes to allow it to equilibrate.

An air bubble is introduced into the open end of the apparatus and the movement of the bubble in a given time period can be recorded. This will measure the rate of water uptake by the plant, which will give a close approximation of the rate of transpiration.

Factors affecting transpiration rate

Temperature

An increase in temperature will increase the kinetic energy of water molecules, which will increase the rate of evaporation from mesophyll cells, therefore increasing the rate of transpiration.

Humidity

An increase in humidity will decrease the rate of transpiration because it will reduce the water potential **gradient** between air spaces and the external atmosphere. Figure 29 shows the difference in water potential between the tissues of the leaf, the sub-stomatal air spaces and the atmosphere outside the leaf.

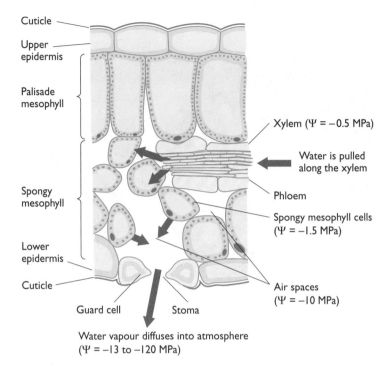

Cuticle

Upper epidermis

Palisade mesophyll

Xylem ($\Psi = -0.5$ MPa)

Water is pulled along the xylem

Spongy mesophyll

Phloem

Spongy mesophyll cells ($\Psi = -1.5$ MPa)

Lower epidermis

Cuticle

Air spaces ($\Psi = -10$ MPa)

Guard cell   Stoma

Water vapour diffuses into atmosphere ($\Psi = -13$ to -120 MPa)

Figure 29 How water moves through leaves

Wind speed

An increased wind speed will increase the rate of transpiration because it will raise the water potential gradient between air spaces and the external atmosphere.

Light intensity

An increase in light intensity will increase the rate of transpiration, as this will cause an opening of the stomata to allow CO_2 to enter the leaf for photosynthesis.

Adaptations of plants to different habitats

Xerophytes

Xerophytes are plants that have adapted to conditions of low water availability. They have adaptations to conserve water by **reducing transpiration**.

For example, the adaptations of *Marram* grass (see Figure 30) include:
- a thick cuticle on the leaves to waterproof the leaf and prevent evaporation through the cuticle
- sunken stomata in pits; hairs surrounding the stomata trap water vapour, maintaining humid air around stomata and reducing the water potential gradient
- hinge cells, which cause the leaves to roll up, again maintaining humid air around stomata and reducing the water potential gradient

Knowledge check 15

Describe two environmental factors that can reduce the rate of transpiration in a plant.

Examiner tip

If the diameter of a tree trunk is lower during the middle of the day (i.e. when both the light intensity and temperature are high) than in the morning and evening, this is due to the increase in rate of transpiration producing negative pressure on the xylem vessels; as a result, their diameter decreases.

Examiner tip

Xerophytes try to reduce the rate of transpiration mainly by reducing the water potential gradient between the sub-stomatal air spaces and the outside atmosphere.

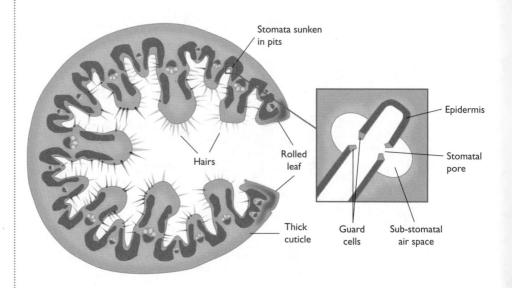

Figure 30 Transverse section of *Marram*

Other xeromorphic adaptations in plants include:
- a rounded shape of the plant or leaf to reduce the surface area-to-volume ratio, reducing the rate of water loss
- reduction of leaves to spines or needles, reducing the surface area for water loss
- ability to fix CO_2 at night, so stomata can be closed during the day.
- a shallow, extensive root system to absorb rainwater
- long taproots to obtain water from sources deep underground

Hydrophytes

Hydrophytes are plants adapted to aquatic environments. Water lilies, for example, live with their roots submerged in mud and leaves floating on the surface. They are adapted in the following ways:
- stomata on the upper epidermis of the leaves to allow gas exchange
- a thin cuticle, as water loss is not problematic
- large air spaces in stem and leaf tissue to provide buoyancy
- poorly developed xylem, as the water provides support

Mesophytes

Mesophytes are terrestrial plants that are adapted to neither a dry nor wet environment. Mesophytes grow well with an adequate water supply, while in prolonged dry periods they survive by shedding their leaves (to reduce transpiration), producing dormant seeds and surviving underground.

Knowledge check 16

Hydrophytes, such as the water lily, do not have a waxy cuticle. True or false?

Translocation of organic compounds

Organic molecules, mainly sucrose, are transported in the **phloem** from where they are produced (**sources**) to where they are utilised or stored (**sinks**). Sucrose shows **bidirectional transport** — it moves both up and down the stem.

The exact mechanism for how organic molecules are transported in the phloem is not clear, but experiments have shown that it is too fast to be by diffusion alone. Different hypotheses have been put forward, including **mass flow** and **cytoplasmic streaming**, but neither can account for all the observations made.

Evidence for translocation

Ringing experiments

Cylinders of bark can be taken from the plant stem — removing the phloem but leaving the xylem intact. The composition of phloem shows that sucrose and other organic solutes are present above the ring but absent from the region below the ring. This indicates that translocation occurs in the phloem rather than in the xylem.

Use of aphids and autoradiography

Aphids, which naturally feed on sap in the phloem, can be used to study the sap contents. Colonies of aphids can be allowed to feed on a plant. While they are feeding, their heads are cut off, leaving their mouthparts inserted into the phloem. The contents of the emerging sap can then be studied.

If the plant is supplied with radioactive carbon dioxide ($^{14}CO_2$) and allowed to photosynthesise, then any carbohydrates it makes, including sucrose, will be radioactively labelled. The movement of these radioactive molecules in the shoot can be traced either by using photographic film or with a Geiger counter.

An **autoradiograph** is an image produced on photographic film — the presence of radioactive isotope will cause the film to 'fog', revealing the location of the labelled carbohydrates. This corresponds to the location of the phloem tissue in the stem.

This technique of using aphid colonies and radioactive tracing has demonstrated that:
- sucrose is transported in the phloem
- sucrose is transported bi-directionally to sinks
- translocation is a rapid process

Summary

After studying this topic you should be able to:
- identify the different tissues within a dicotyledon root and stem
- describe the structure of xylem and phloem as seen by the light and electron microscope
- describe and explain how water and mineral ions are absorbed and transported across the root
- describe the structure, and explain the role, of endodermis
- describe the different theories to explain the movement of water from root to leaf
- explain how different environmental factors affect transpiration and describe how these effects can be measured experimentally
- explain how the adaptations shown by different angiosperms enable them to survive in different habitats
- use experimental evidence to support the different theories relating to the translocation of organic materials from source to sink

Transport systems in animals

Key concepts you must understand
- As organisms get larger their surface area-to-volume ratio decreases and diffusion distances increase.
- Large organisms require vascular (transport) systems because diffusion is inefficient over large distances.
- **Mass transport** is the bulk movement of substances through a transport system using force.
- There are two basic types of vascular system in animals:
  - An **open circulation** consists of a fluid-filled body cavity (called the haemocoel), as seen in insects.
  - In a **closed circulation** the heart pumps blood, under high pressure, through **blood vessels**; organs are not in direct contact with the blood. Respiratory gases are transported in blood by a respiratory pigment like **haemoglobin**. Annelids and vertebrates have a closed circulation.

Single and double circulations

Figure 31(a) shows a **single circulation** in a fish:
- Blood passes through the heart once every time it passes around the body.
- Blood leaves the heart under high pressure, but the pressure must fall before it reaches the gill capillaries.
- The blood then flows slowly, under low pressure, around the rest of the body before returning to the heart.

Figure 31(b) shows a **double circulation** in a mammal:
- Blood must pass through the heart twice every time it goes round the body once.
  - The **pulmonary circulation** transports blood between the heart and the lungs.
  - The **systemic circulation** transports blood between the heart and all the other organs of the body.
- The blood flows quickly, under high pressure, in both the pulmonary and systemic circulations.

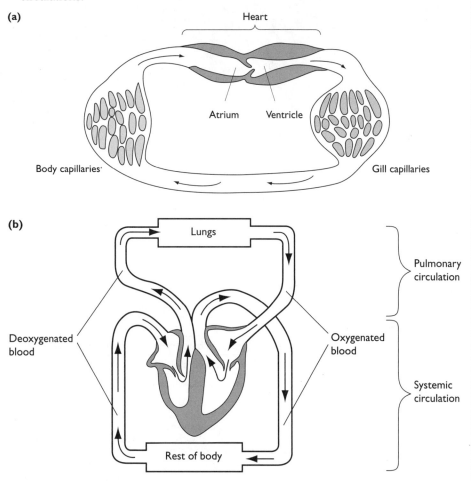

Figure 31 (a) The fish circulatory system; (b) The mammalian circulatory system

The heart

The mammalian heart is a four-chambered **pump** situated in the thoracic cavity (Figure 32). It is a specialised organ and consists mainly of **cardiac muscle**. The structure of the heart allows the complete separation of oxygenated and deoxygenated blood.

Knowledge check 19

Explain why the left ventricle has a thicker muscular wall than the right ventricle.

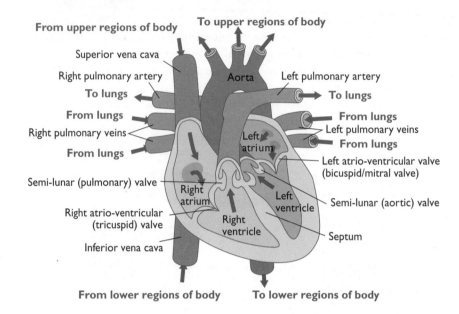

Figure 32 The internal structure of the heart

Table 10 shows the functions of the different structures in the mammalian heart.

Knowledge check 20

Figure 33 shows the position of the coronary arteries. What is their function?

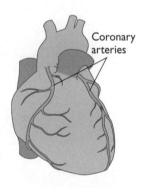

Figure 33 The position of the coronary arteries

Table 10 The functions of the different structures in the mammalian heart

Structure	Function
Pulmonary artery	Carries deoxygenated blood to lungs from right ventricle
Pulmonary vein	Carries oxygenated blood from lungs to left atrium
Aorta	Carries oxygenated blood from left ventricle to body tissues
Vena cava	Carries deoxygenated blood from body to right atrium
Atria	Thin walled chambers, which receive blood
Ventricles	Thick walled chambers to generate high pressure in blood when walls contract in order to force blood over a great distance; note: the left ventricle is larger with a thicker muscular wall than the right ventricle to generate a higher pressure so that blood can travel the greater distance to the extremities of the body
Atrio-ventricular valves	Prevent back-flow of blood from the ventricles to the atria during ventricular systole
Valve tendons ('heart strings')	Keep valves under tension and prevent them from inverting during ventricular systole
Semi-lunar valves	Prevent back-flow of blood from the arteries to the ventricles (the only examples of valves in arteries)

The cardiac cycle

Figure 34 shows the sequence of events that takes place during the cardiac cycle.

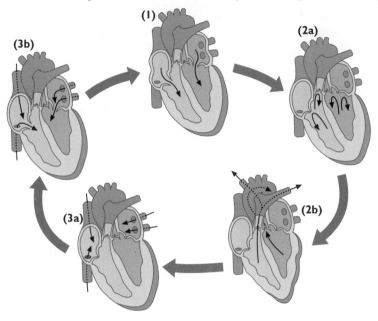

Figure 34 The stages of the cardiac cycle

Atrial systole

- As the atria contract, atrial pressure exceeds ventricular pressure — the atrio-ventricular valves open and blood flows from the atria to the ventricles (stage 1).

Ventricular systole

- As the ventricles contract, the ventricular pressure exceeds atrial pressure, causing the atrio-ventricular valves to close and generating the first heart sound — 'lub' (stage 2a).
- When ventricular pressure exceeds aortic pressure, the semi-lunar valves open and blood flows from the ventricle into the arteries (stage 2b).

Atrial and ventricular diastole

- As the ventricles relax, ventricular pressure falls below the pressure in the arteries causing the semi-lunar valves to close, generating the second heart sound — 'dup'.
- Low-pressure blood in the veins returns to the heart as the atria relax (stage 3a).
- When ventricular pressure falls below atrial pressure, the atrio-ventricular valve opens again and blood flows from the atria to the ventricles (stage 3b).

Examiner tip

When describing any of the phases in the cardiac cycle you must make reference to:
- which chamber is contracting and which is relaxing, and relate this to the relative pressures in both chambers
- which valve is open and which valve is closed

The cardiac cycle can be analysed graphically, as shown in Figure 35.

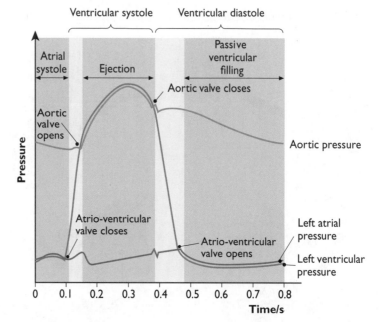

Figure 35 Pressure changes associated with the cardiac cycle

The cardiac impulse

- Cardiac muscle is myogenic.
- The cardiac impulse (heart beat) originates in the **sino-atrial node** (**SAN**), which acts as a **pacemaker** and is located in the wall of the right atrium.
- The impulse spreads out into the walls of the atria causing **atrial systole**.
- There is a layer of non-conductive connective tissue that prevents the impulse from travelling down the wall of the ventricles.

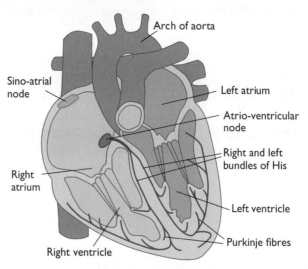

Figure 36 The conducting system of the heart includes the SAN, AVN and Purkinje fibres

- The impulse is picked up by the **atrio-ventricular node** (**AVN**), which is also located in the wall of the right atrium at its base.
- The impulse is then conducted through the **bundles of His** to the apex of the ventricles.
- The impulse then travels upwards through the branching **Purkinje fibres** through the walls of the ventricles, causing the cardiac muscle of the ventricles to contract (**systole**) *from the bottom upwards*.

Control of cardiac activity

At rest the heart beats at approximately 75 beats per minute. During periods of activity/ inactivity the heart rate can be varied by nerves originating from the cardiovascular centre in the medulla of the brain. Impulses can be sent via different neurons to either stimulate the SAN, increasing heart rate, or to inhibit the SAN, decreasing heart rate. These changes to heart rate are **involuntary** and not under conscious control.

The hormone **adrenalin**, released when your body is under stress, also causes the SAN to discharge at a higher frequency, increasing heart rate.

Blood vessels

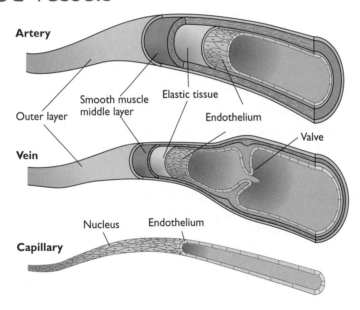

Figure 37 Structure of an artery, a vein and a capillary

There are five types of blood vessel:
- **Arteries** transport blood away from the heart.
- **Arterioles** connect arteries to capillaries.
- **Capillaries** are microscopic vessels that form networks within the tissues of the body.
- **Venules** connect capillaries to veins.
- **Veins** transport blood back to the heart.

Table 11 Summary of the main structural differences between arteries, veins and capillaries

Feature	Artery	Vein	Capillary
Outer (protective) layer	Present with collagen fibres	Present with collagen fibres	Absent
Middle layer	Thick layer with smooth muscle and many elastic fibres	Thin layer with smooth muscle and few elastic fibres	Absent — no muscle or elastic tissue
Endothelium (smooth to reduce friction)	Present	Present	Present
Pressure	High	Low	Low

Arteries and arterioles

As a result of ventricular systole blood enters the large arteries under high pressure; arteries have thick walls to resist this pressure. They contain many elastic fibres, which stretch to allow the large arteries to bulge to accommodate the blood.

The pressure in these arteries shows a rhythmic rise and fall (which corresponds to ventricular systole and diastole), generating a pulsatile flow. **Elastic recoil** of the elastic fibres pushes blood along the artery and produces an even flow of blood through the arteries.

Knowledge check 23

Explain the importance of vasoconstriction and vasodilation to a mammal.

In the smaller arteries and arterioles the smooth muscle fibres can contract and relax, which can change the diameter of the lumen and therefore help to control blood flow to different parts of the body:

- When the smooth muscle contracts this causes vasoconstriction (the lumen becomes narrower) and restricts the blood-flow.
- When the smooth muscle relaxes this causes vasodilation (the lumen becomes wider) and increases the blood-flow.

Examiner tip

The aorta has a high proportion of elastic fibres. During ventricular systole they allow the aorta to stretch, to accommodate the blood entering; then during diastole they recoil to maintain blood pressure and force blood along the artery. Do not confuse the properties of elastic fibres and muscle — elastic fibres cannot contract, they can only stretch and recoil.

Figure 38 The changes in blood pressure at different places in the systemic circulation during ventricular systole and diastole (not drawn to scale)

As the blood travels further from the heart the blood vessels become increasingly branched, and the blood pressure and rate of blood flow decrease. This is due to:
- the increase in total cross-sectional area of the blood vessels
- frictional resistance to blood flowing along the blood vessels

Capillaries

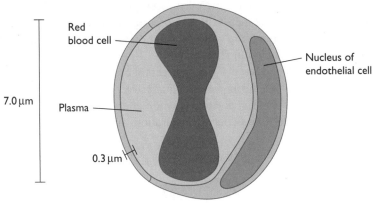

Figure 39 Cross-section of a capillary

The millions of capillaries in our bodies act as **exchange surfaces**. Table 12 shows the characteristics of capillaries and how they are adapted to carry out exchange of materials.

Table 12 The characteristics of a capillary

Structural adaptation	Advantage
Form a dense network	Large surface area for diffusion
Capillary walls are one cell thick and flattened	Short diffusion pathway
Small diameter/narrow	
Red blood cells in contact with wall	
Narrow lumen	Reduces flow rate as red blood cells pass singly, giving more time for diffusion
Capillary walls permeable to gases	O_2 and CO_2 can easily diffuse into/out of the blood
Capillary walls contain pores between the endothelial cells	Allows the formation of tissue fluid

Venules and veins

The return of blood to the heart is non-rhythmic. **Semi-lunar valves** in the veins prevent backflow. Although the pressure in veins is low, blood is returned to the heart due to:

- pressure increases caused by skeletal muscle (see Figure 40):
  - When skeletal muscles (surrounding the vein) contract they squeeze the vein, reducing the volume and increasing the pressure inside the vein.
  - This forces blood through the valve 'in front of' the blood and causes the valve behind to close, so preventing backflow.
  - This ensures that blood travels in one direction only.
- residual pressure of blood during ventricular systole
- negative pressure due to atrial diastole (suction effect)
- negative pressure in the thorax during inspiration (suction effect)

Examiner tip

When answering questions on blood vessels it is always important to link the structure of the vessel with its function.

Knowledge check 24

Figure 40 shows a vein surrounded by bone and skeletal muscle. When the muscle contracts, state the direction in which blood will flow, which valve will be open and which valve will be closed.

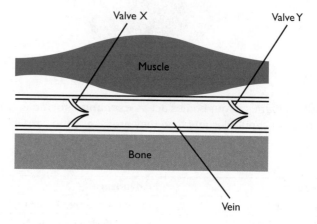

Figure 40 A vein surrounded by bone and skeletal muscle

Blood

Blood is made up of **plasma** (55%) and **cells** (45%). Plasma consists of 90% water; the other 10% is made up of solutes, for example glucose and amino acids. Plasma proteins are also dissolved in plasma and are important in the formation of tissue fluid. The function of plasma is to transport the soluble products of digestion as well as hormones, proteins, albumin, fibrinogen, antibodies and ions. It also distributes heat.

Red blood cells are responsible for transporting respiratory gases around the body. **White blood cells** are involved in protecting the body against infection — immunity. **Platelets** are involved in blood clotting.

The formation of tissue fluid

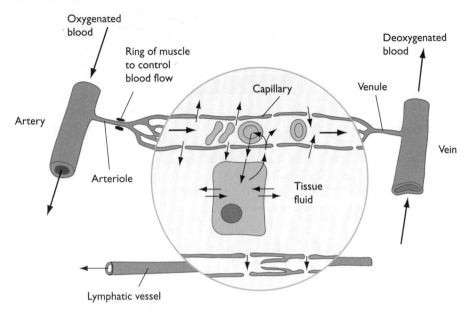

Figure 41 Blood flow through a capillary bed

The capillary wall is made up of a single layer of endothelial cells and is porous, i.e. there are minute pores (also known as fenestrations) between the individual cells.

At the arterial end of the capillary the hydrostatic pressure is relatively high (caused by ventricular systole) and this causes ultrafiltration to occur:
- Fluid (water and small solutes) is forced out of the blood.
- The larger plasma proteins and cells remain in the blood as they are too big to pass through the pores (Figure 41).

The fluid forced out of the blood is now called **tissue fluid** and it bathes the cells in essential nutrients. As fluid is forced out of the capillary the hydrostatic pressure in the capillary falls.

At the venule end of the capillary the water potential of the blood is lower than that of the tissue fluid due to the soluble plasma proteins. This causes water to be drawn back into the capillary by osmosis.

Figure 42 shows that at the arteriole end of the capillary the hydrostatic pressure is greater than osmotic pressure, so fluid is forced out into the tissues. At the venule end of the capillary the hydrostatic pressure is lower than the osmotic pressure, so water is drawn back into the blood.

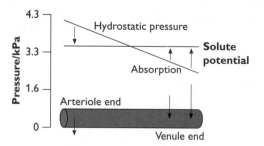

Figure 42 Relationship between hydrostatic pressure and solute potential

Examiner tip

It is easy to lose marks in the exam for incorrect terminology. Many students make reference to blood being forced out of the capillary; this is incorrect — *fluid* is forced out of the capillary at the arteriole end of the capillary. You should refer to *water* moving back into the capillary at the venule end, because osmosis is involved.

Knowledge check 25

Describe how fluid that has been forced out of the capillary is returned to the blood.

More fluid leaves the capillaries than is reabsorbed. Excess tissue fluid drains into blind-ended capillaries of the **lymphatic system**. Here lymph capillaries join to form lymph vessels, which return the lymph to the blood in the veins of the neck. Lymph vessels also have valves to ensure one-way flow.

Transport of oxygen

Oxygen is transported around the body in red blood cells. Red blood cells have many adaptations to increase the efficiency of this transport (see Figure 39). They have a large surface area-to-volume ratio because:

- they are very small (about $8\,\mu m$ in diameter)
- they lack a nucleus, giving them a biconcave disc shape

The lack of a nucleus and other organelles means that more haemoglobin (Hb) can be contained within the cytoplasm of the cell. Haemoglobin is a globular protein, with a quaternary structure (Figure 43). It is made up of four polypeptide chains — each contains a haem group. The haem group contains iron ions (Fe^{2+}), which form a lose association with O_2 molecules. As there are four haem groups, each molecule of Hb can transport four molecules of oxygen.

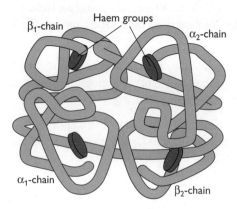

Figure 43 The quaternary structure of haemoglobin

When Hb combines with O_2 it is called oxyhaemoglobin — this reaction is reversible:

$$Hb \ + \ 4O_2 \ \rightleftharpoons \ HbO_8$$

Haemoglobin   Oxyhaemoglobin

Haemoglobin should be thought of as an 'O$_2$ taxi'. It picks up — **loads** — O$_2$ in the lungs and drops off — **unloads** — O$_2$ at the tissues where it is needed for respiration.

The oxygen–haemoglobin dissociation curve

This oxygen–haemoglobin dissociation curve (Figure 44) shows the relationship between the partial pressure of oxygen (pO_2) and the percentage saturation of Hb with O$_2$.

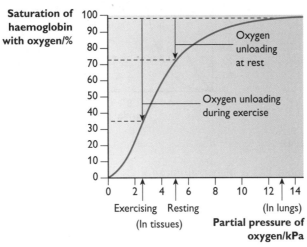

Figure 44 Oxygen dissociation curve of human haemoglobin

The shape of the curve is significant:

- The curve is S-shaped, which indicates that Hb is efficient at loading O$_2$ and can become fully saturated at a lower pO_2 than if the relationship was a linear one.
- Hb has a high affinity for O$_2$ at a relatively high partial pressures of O$_2$ and will therefore load O$_2$ to form oxyhaemoglobin. This occurs in the capillaries of the lungs.
- Hb has a low affinity for O$_2$ in low pO_2 and will therefore unload O$_2$. This occurs in the capillaries of the tissues.
- The steep part of the curve means that for a small decrease in the pO_2 there will be a large decrease in the percentage saturation of haemoglobin with O$_2$. This means more O$_2$ will be unloaded to the tissues to carry out aerobic respiration.

From Figure 44 you can see that for a drop in pO_2 of 2.5 kPa (tissues at rest to tissues exercising) the percentage saturation of haemoglobin falls by about 40%, i.e. 40% more O$_2$ is unloaded to the tissues for respiration.

Examiner tip

Many students tend to focus on haemoglobin's ability to load oxygen. However it is the unloading of oxygen by haemoglobin that is crucial — oxygen is unloaded to the tissues so they can carry out aerobic respiration.

Fetal haemoglobin and other respiratory pigments

Figure 45 shows that the oxygen dissociation curve for fetal haemoglobin is situated to the left of that for 'normal' adult haemoglobin.

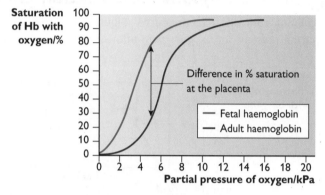

Figure 45 The oxygen dissociation curves of fetal and adult haemoglobin

Fetal haemoglobin has a higher affinity for O_2 — at any given pO_2 the percentage saturation of Hb is higher. The significance of this is that the maternal haemoglobin will unload approximately 70% of its O_2 to the tissues of the placenta; the fetal haemoglobin will then load O_2 from the placenta to become approximately 80% saturated.

Organisms that live in low O_2 environments, for example llamas (at high altitude) and lugworms (in burrows in sand) also have pigments with a higher affinity for oxygen — i.e. a dissociation curve to the left. The advantage of this is that they can pick up more O_2 and become fully saturated at a lower pO_2.

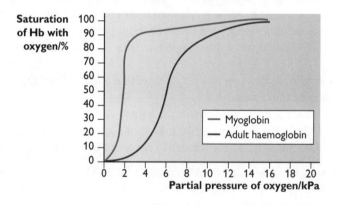

Figure 46 The dissociation curve for myoglobin

The Bohr effect

During exercise the muscles are working harder so they need more ATP. Therefore the rate of respiration increases. This also produces more CO_2, which lowers the pH of the blood. This causes the dissociation curve to shift to the right — the Bohr effect (Figure 47).

The Hb now has a lower affinity for O_2 — at any given pO_2 the percentage saturation of Hb is lower. The advantage is that Hb gives up more O_2 to the muscle tissues for an increased rate of respiration.

Knowledge check 26

Figure 46 shows the dissociation curve for myoglobin, the respiratory pigment found in muscle fibres. Use the diagram to explain the function of myoglobin.

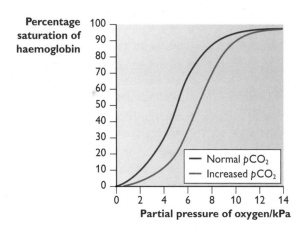

Figure 47 The Bohr effect

Transport of carbon dioxide

Some CO_2 is transported in red blood cells. The majority of CO_2 is transported as **bicarbonate ions** (HCO_3^-) in the plasma. CO_2 diffuses into the red blood cell and combines with H_2O to form carbonic acid (H_2CO_3). This reaction is catalysed by the enzyme **carbonic anhydrase** (Figure 48).

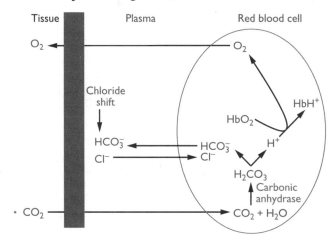

Figure 48 A red blood cell showing the biochemical pathway involved in transporting CO_2

The carbonic acid then dissociates into protons (H^+) and bicarbonate ions (HCO_3^-). The H^+ will lower the pH of the cell and so it needs to be buffered — this is done by haemoglobin. The oxyhaemoglobin therefore dissociates, unloading O_2, which diffuses out of the red blood cell and into the tissues. The accumulation of HCO_3^- causes these ions to diffuse out into the plasma.

Electroneutrality is maintained by the inward diffusion of chloride ions from the plasma. This is known as the **chloride shift**.

In the capillaries of lungs all of these reactions occur in reverse.

Knowledge check 27

Use Figure 48 to state the function of the hydrogen ions produced in the red blood cell and explain its importance for body tissues.

Summary

After studying this topic you should be able to:

- compare the vascular systems of animal groups — insects, annelids and vertebrates
- describe the differences between an open circulatory system and a closed circulatory system
- explain why the double circulatory system of a mammal is more efficient compared with the single circulation of a fish
- state the names of the main blood vessels associated with the human heart
- describe the structure of the heart and relate this to its function
- describe the events of the cardiac cycle and be able to interpret graphical analysis of pressure changes involved
- describe the role of sino-atrial node and Purkinje fibres in generating and transmitting the cardiac impulse
- describe the structure of different types of blood vessel and relate this to their function
- describe the function of plasma in relation to the transport of nutrients, hormones, excretory products and heat
- describe how tissue fluid is formed and explain its importance in exchange
- describe and explain the function of red blood cells and plasma in relation to transport of respiratory gases
- describe the oxygen–haemoglobin dissociation curves for a mammal (adult and fetus)
- compare the oxygen dissociation curves of animals adapted to low-oxygen habitats
- describe and explain the Bohr effect and chloride shift in relation to the transport of carbon dioxide

Reproductive strategies

Key concepts you must understand

- Reproduction is one of the seven characteristics of living organisms.
- A species will continue to exist as long as its members produce offspring that live long enough to have offspring of their own.
- The production of offspring that are genetically identical to their parents (i.e. clones) allows a species to rapidly colonise a stable environment.
- In a changing environment, the survival of a species depends on its ability to produce offspring that are genetically different from their parents.
- There are two types of reproduction: **asexual reproduction** and **sexual reproduction**.

Asexual reproduction (cloning)

Asexual reproduction involves only one individual. It produces offspring that are genetically identical to their parent and each other, i.e. they are **clones**. There are different types of asexual reproduction, but they all involve the process of **mitosis**.

The advantages of reproducing asexually (by mitosis) are as follows:
- It produces clones (if one is successful they are all successful).
- It requires less energy as a mate does not need to be found.
- It is relatively fast and can produce rapid population growth.
- It allows the species to colonise a stable environment and is a good strategy when environmental conditions are favourable.

However, there are disadvantages to reproducing asexually. When environmental conditions change or a new disease enters the population the species may become

Knowledge check 28

There may be some genetic variation between individuals in a population of organisms that reproduce asexually. What causes this genetic variation to occur?

extinct. This is due to the lack of genetic diversity within the population; all the individuals will be equally susceptible.

Sexual reproduction

Sexual reproduction usually involves two individuals (of the same species) or one organism if they are hermaphrodites, for example tapeworms and angiosperms. It involves the formation of **haploid gametes** (see Table 13) by **meiosis** and fusion of the gametes during **fertilisation** to produce a **diploid zygote**.

Sexual reproduction produces offspring that are genetically different from their parents and each other.

Table 13 Comparison of the male and female gametes in animals

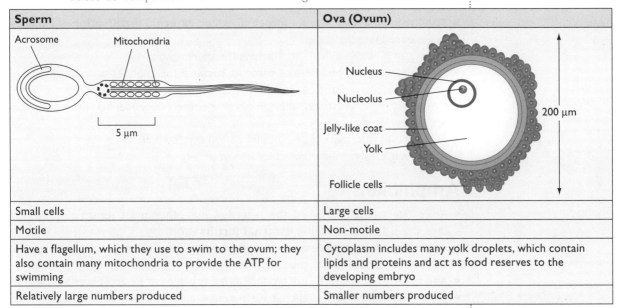

Sperm	Ova (Ovum)
Small cells	Large cells
Motile	Non-motile
Have a flagellum, which they use to swim to the ovum; they also contain many mitochondria to provide the ATP for swimming	Cytoplasm includes many yolk droplets, which contain lipids and proteins and act as food reserves to the developing embryo
Relatively large numbers produced	Smaller numbers produced

The advantages of reproducing sexually (involving meiosis) are as follows:
- It is a good strategy when environmental conditions are changeable.
- It produces genetic variation within a population.
- Some offspring will survive the unfavourable conditions, which allows the species to adapt by natural selection.
- It can involve the production of a resistant stage in the life cycle, such as seeds, which can be dispersed far away, thus reducing competition between the parent and the offspring.

Examiner tip

Individual organisms, or offspring, are unable to adapt to changes in the environment. Natural selection allows a *species* to adapt to a changing environment.

However, sexual reproduction is relatively slow and energetically expensive. In animals, individuals have to spend time finding a mate and engage in elaborate courtship rituals. They produce large numbers of gametes, the majority of which are never fertilised and are therefore wasted.

Many plants produce large, brightly coloured petals and provide nectar for pollinating insects. If they are wind pollinated they have to produce large quantities of pollen grains, the majority of which will be wasted.

Some organisms, such as the water flea (*Daphnia*), reproduce asexually during stable environmental conditions; however, a change in the environment triggers them into reproducing sexually.

Reproductive strategies in vertebrates

All vertebrates reproduce sexually; however, different groups of vertebrates have different strategies in terms of:

- how fertilisation is brought about
- the development of the embryo
- the degree of parental care given to the offspring

Fish

- Fish live in an aquatic environment and exhibit **external fertilisation** — gametes are released into the water.
- The water provides a medium in which the sperm can swim.
- Fish produce large numbers of gametes because the chances of fertilisation are quite low — many gametes are eaten or are carried away by the current.
- If fertilisation occurs, the resulting embryo is entirely dependent on the yolk supply for its development.
- As a general rule, there is no parental care shown by fish.
- As a result, many embryos will be eaten or perish.

Amphibians

- Amphibians have colonised the land; however, they must return to water to reproduce. They also exhibit **external fertilisation**.
- Amphibians have a tendency to 'couple' during reproduction — this increases the chances of fertilisation as the sperm and the ova are released in close proximity.
- As a result, amphibians do not produce as many gametes because fewer are wasted.
- Most amphibians show little or no parental care and therefore produce large numbers of embryos which are entirely dependent on the yolk for their development.

Reptiles and birds

- Both these groups have successfully colonised the land and do not need to return to water to reproduce.
- The evolution of an intromittent organ and **internal fertilisation** has allowed this to happen.
- With internal fertilisation fusion of gametes occurs inside the female's body.
- This greatly increases the chances of fertilisation and as a result low numbers of gametes are produced.
- The developing embryo is encased in an **amniotic egg**, which is then laid by the female.

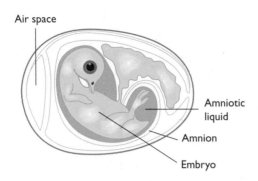

Figure 49 An amniotic egg

- The amniotic egg is permeable to gases and waterproof, so prevents desiccation of the embryo (reptile eggs are covered in a soft, leathery shell and bird's eggs are covered in a hard, calcareous shell).
- The embryo is dependent on the yolk for its development (the larger the egg the more developed the offspring will be when it hatches).
- Reptiles tend to produce large numbers of eggs (though far fewer than amphibians) and show little parental care (e.g. turtles).
- Birds tend to lay fewer eggs and show a large amount of parental care. This increases the chances of the offspring reaching reproductive age.

Mammals

- Mammals also carry out **internal fertilisation**.
- Low numbers of gametes are produced because the chances of fertilisation are high.
- In placental mammals the embryo gains nourishment from its mother's blood via the placenta.
- The embryo develops inside its mother's **uterus** and is therefore protected from predators or adverse weather conditions.
- The young are born at a relatively advanced state of development — antelopes can stand within minutes and can run within hours of being born.
- Mammals show a high degree of parental care, which increases the chances of the offspring reaching sexual maturity. As a result, they have low numbers of offspring.

Summary

- In general, as the vertebrate groups have evolved from fish to amphibians to reptiles to birds and mammals, the following changes have taken place:
  - a change from external fertilisation to internal fertilisation
  - a reduction in the numbers of gametes produced
  - a reduction in the number of offspring produced
  - an increase in the degree of parental care given to offspring
- Fish have evolved a strategy of investing their energy into producing large numbers of gametes to produce large numbers of embryos — the vast majority will die.
- Birds and mammals have evolved a strategy of investing their energy into producing few offspring and giving a higher degree of parental care.
- In a sexually reproducing species two offspring need to survive to reproductive age to maintain the population.

Examiner tip

The proportion of yolk in a bird's egg gives an indication of the degree of development of the offspring before hatching and the level of parental care given. For example, a duck's egg has a relatively large yolk (about 35% of the egg mass) and when the duckling hatches it has a covering of down and is able to walk and leave the nest immediately. A starling's egg has a smaller yolk (about 17% of the egg mass) and when the chick hatches it is naked and unable to stand, so it needs a higher degree of parental care than the duckling.

Knowledge check 29

Explain what is meant by the term internal fertilisation and describe the two main advantages to organisms reproducing in this way.

Reproductive strategies in insects

- Insects have evolved many adaptations to colonise terrestrial habitats and one of these is the use of **internal fertilisation**.
- Most species lay eggs, coated with a waterproof layer to prevent desiccation.
- The life cycles of insects differ. Species either show **complete** or **incomplete metamorphosis**.

Complete metamorphosis

In complete metamorphosis there are four distinct stages in the life cycle:
- the **egg** stage
- the **larval** stage (e.g. a caterpillar or maggot) — designed to eat
- the **pupal** stage (where they undergo complete metamorphosis)
- the **adult** (or **imago**) stage (e.g. a butterfly of housefly) — designed for sex

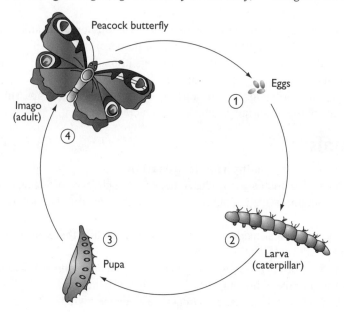

Figure 50 Butterfly life cycle

Incomplete metamorphosis

In incomplete metamorphosis there are three distinct stages in the life cycle:
- the **egg** stage
- the **nymph** stages — nymphs resemble the adult and progress through a series of developmental stages (called **instars**) to become the adult
- the **adult** (or imago) stage

Knowledge check 30

Describe the main differences between complete and incomplete metamorphosis.

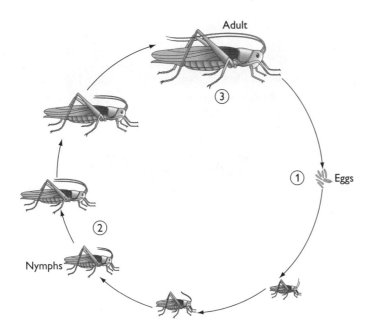

Figure 51 Grasshopper life cycle

Reproductive strategies in flowering plants

Flowering plants: angiosperms

- The flowering plants (angiosperms) are the most successful group of plants. Their colonisation of terrestrial habitats is closely linked to the evolution of insects.
- Flowering plants can reproduce both **asexually** and **sexually**, which has contributed to their success.
- To be able to colonise terrestrial habitats plants, like animals, have had to evolve strategies for the male gamete to reach, and fuse with, the female gamete without the need for water.
- The reproductive organ of an angiosperm is the flower. The 'male part' of the flower is the stamen where the male gametes (**pollen grains**) are formed in the anther. The 'female part' of the flower is the carpel where the female gamete (the **egg cell**) is formed within an ovule.

Examiner tip
Most flowering plants are hermaphrodites, i.e. they posses both male and female reproductive organs. Many flowering plants are also capable of self-fertilisation — but this is not the same as reproducing asexually.

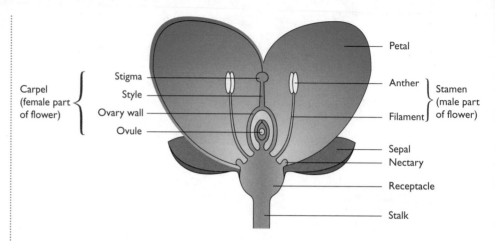

Figure 52 Structure of a flower

Pollination

Pollination is the transfer of pollen from one plant to another. The pollen grains have a hard outer coat, which prevents desiccation.

Pollination can occur either by wind or by animals such as insects. Wind pollination is inefficient and therefore wind-pollinated plants must produce vast quantities of pollen to ensure pollination is successful.

Insect-pollinated flowers have large, colourful petals and attractive scents. They also produce large quantities of pollen, or nectar. This attracts insects to the flowers to feed; as they feed, pollen gets stuck to the insect bodies. When the animal moves to another flower (of a plant of the same species) the pollen will be deposited on the stigma. The pollen grain travels down a pollen tube to reach the egg cell; this also enables fertilisation to occur without water.

Insect pollination increases the chances of successful pollination and this exploitation of insects has aided the successful colonisation of land by angiosperms.

Seed formation and dispersal

After fertilisation:
- the fertilised egg cell develops into a plant embryo
- the ovule develops into a **seed**

The seed is surrounded by the **testa** (a tough, resistant coat), which protects the seed against adverse environmental conditions. The seed also contains a food store, which enables the embryo to develop and grow large enough to emerge above ground and produce leaves so that it can begin to photosynthesise.

In many species of plant the seed is encased within a fruit, which results in the seeds being dispersed by animals. Animals eat the fruits but the seeds cannot be digested owing to the protective testa and so they pass out with the animal's faeces.

Knowledge check 31

State one advantage and one disadvantage of insect pollination in plants.

Examiner tip

The testa does not protect the seed from desiccation; seeds are already desiccated as this allows them to survive during a period of dormancy. The testa therefore protects them from harsh environmental conditions such as the digestive secretions in the gut of animals that disperse the seeds.

After studying this topic you should be able to:
- describe the differences between, and explain the relative advantages and disadvantages of, asexual and sexual reproduction in organisms
- describe the differences between the gametes produced by males and females
- describe the difference between internal and external fertilisation
- explain the strategies employed by vertebrates that have allowed them to colonise terrestrial habitats, with reference to the development of the zygote and the degree of parental care
- use insects as an example of a successful land-colonising animal group and describe the differences between incomplete and complete metamorphosis
- compare reproductive strategies in plants and animals
- explain the strategies employed by angiosperms that have allowed them to colonise terrestrial habitats, and describe the link between angiosperms and insects

Summary

Adaptations for nutrition

Key concepts you must understand

- Organisms are referred to as either autotrophs or heterotrophs depending on their nutrition.
- Autotrophs are organisms that synthesise complex organic molecules from simple inorganic molecules, using a source of energy.
- Plants are autotrophs. They convert carbon dioxide (CO_2) and water (H_2O) into glucose ($C_6H_{12}O_6$) using light energy during photosynthesis.
- Heterotrophs are organisms that feed on complex organic molecules.
- These complex organic molecules tend to be large, insoluble molecules such as polysaccharides (like starch) and proteins, which cannot cross plasma membranes.
- Chemical digestion using enzymes is necessary to hydrolyse these molecules into small, soluble molecules, such as glucose and amino acids, which can then be **absorbed** and **assimilated** into other molecules that the organism requires.
- Many animals, including humans, consume complex organic molecules and break them down in the gut; this is known as holozoic nutrition.
- Saprophytes carry out extracellular digestion to obtain nutrition from dead organic matter, i.e. dead organisms and animal waste (urine and faeces).

Nutrition in animals

Animals are heterotrophs and the majority have a digestive system — referred to as the **alimentary canal** or **gut**. The complexity of the gut depends on the variety of food consumed:

- If they feed on only one type of food (e.g. a butterfly feeding on nectar) then the gut is undifferentiated.
- If they feed on a variety of food sources then the gut is differentiated, with each region becoming specialised to carry out a particular function.

Nutrition in animals can be broken down into four stages:

1 Ingestion

- Taking in of food.

2 Digestion

- **Mechanical digestion** reduces the size of the food material, increasing its total surface area and making chemical digestion more efficient.
- **Chemical digestion** involves the hydrolysis of large, insoluble molecules (polymers) into small, soluble molecules (monomers), using **enzymes**.

3 Absorption

- The passage of small soluble molecules (monomers) and other useful substances into the bloodstream.

4 Egestion

- The elimination of undigested food material from the body.

Examiner tip

Do not confuse egestion, which is the elimination of material from a body cavity, with excretion, which is the elimination of the waste products of metabolism from within the body's cells.

Structure of the mammalian gut/alimentary canal

The gut is a long tube that runs through the body (Figure 53).

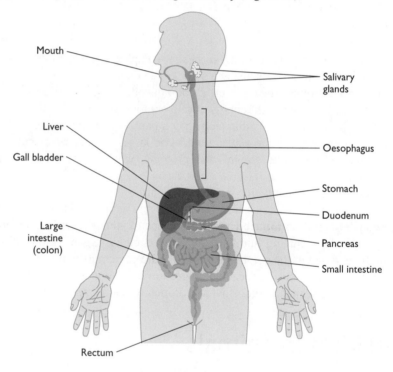

Figure 53 The human gut

The gut walls have the same layers throughout, but they are adapted, in the different regions, to carry out particular functions. The basic structure is shown in Figure 54.

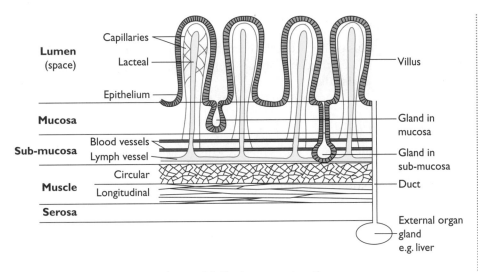

Figure 54 The human gut wall

Table 14 summarises the functions of the different tissues in the gut wall.

Table 14 The functions of the different tissues within the mammalian gut wall

Epithelium	Single layer of cells lining the gut wall
Mucosa	Contains glands that produce digestive secretions: • digestive enzymes • acidic/alkaline fluid to provide the optimum pH for digestive enzymes • mucus (secreted by goblet cells) provide lubrication and protection to the gut wall
Sub-mucosa	Contains blood vessels and lymph vessels for the transport of the soluble products of digestion Contains glands that produce alkaline fluid
Circular muscles and longitudinal muscles	Antagonistic muscle pair — bring about peristalsis due to contraction of the circular muscle behind the bolus of food.
Serosa	Tough, protective coat surrounding the gut.

External organs such as the **salivary glands**, **pancreas** and **liver** also provide digestive secretions, which enter the gut via ducts.

The regions of the gut

The mouth/buccal cavity (pH 6.5–7.5)

- **Mechanical digestion** occurs — using the teeth to increase the surface area of food by reducing its size.
- **Chemical digestion** of **starch** occurs.
- Salivary glands produce **amylase**, **mineral ions** and **mucus**.

The oesophagus

- Transfers the bolus of food from the buccal cavity to the stomach.
- Contraction of the circular muscle behind the bolus of food pushes it downwards — **peristalsis**.
- **Goblet cells** in the mucosa secrete **mucus** to provide lubrication.

The stomach (pH 2)

- **Mechanical digestion** occurs — there are three layers of muscle that churn food into liquid chyme.
- **Chemical digestion** of **proteins** begins.
- Gastric glands secrete:
  - endopeptidases
  - HCl to provide the optimum pH for endopeptidases, to kill any bacteria that have been ingested and to activate the endopeptidases
  - alkaline mucus to protect the stomach wall from the acid and endopeptidases

The small intestine — the duodenum and ileum (pH 7–8.5)

- Main site of **chemical digestion**.
- **Intestinal glands** in the wall of the duodenum produce digestive **enzymes** and **alkaline fluid**. The **pancreas** also secretes enzymes and alkaline fluid into the duodenum via the pancreatic duct. The alkaline fluid neutralises the acidic chyme from the stomach and provides the optimum pH for the digestive enzymes.
- The ileum is the main site of **absorption** of the soluble products of digestion.

Knowledge check 32

Explain why mechanical digestion is important to an animal.

The colon and rectum (large intestine)

- The colon absorbs water and vitamins.
- The rectum is for the temporary storage of faeces.

Chemical digestion in the mammalian gut

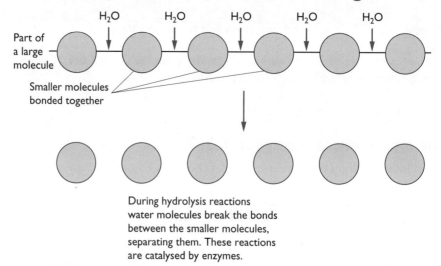

Figure 55 Digestion involves the hydrolysis of polymers into monomers

Chemical digestion of starch

- Starch is **hydrolysed** into maltose by **amylase** (optimum pH 8).
- Amylase is found in **saliva**, and **pancreatic juice** (which is released into the duodenum).
- Maltose is then broken down to glucose by **maltase**.
- Maltase is located on the **cell surface membrane** of the epithelial cells of the small intestine.

Chemical digestion of lipids

- Lipids are mechanically broken down by **bile salts** and chemically digested by **lipase**.
- **Bile** produced in the liver is stored in the gall bladder and secreted into the duodenum. Bile contains:
  - **bile salts**, which **emulsify** the lipids — mechanically break down large lipid drops into smaller droplets; this increases the surface area for the action of lipases
  - alkaline fluid containing $NaHCO_3$ to **neutralise** the stomach acid, giving an **optimum pH** for lipase
- **Lipases**, found in pancreatic juice, hydrolyse lipids into fatty acids and glycerol (some monoglycerides are also produced).

Examiner tip

Many students think that bile salts are enzymes and hydrolyse lipids. This is wrong — bile salts only emulsify lipids, they do not alter them chemically.

Chemical digestion of proteins

- **Endopeptidases** hydrolyse peptide bonds within the polypeptide chain to produce shorter polypeptide chains (peptides). Endopeptidases are found in gastric juice (e.g. pepsin — optimum pH 2) and pancreatic juice (e.g. trypsin — optimum pH 8).
- **Exopeptidases** hydrolyse the terminal peptide bonds at the ends of the polypeptide chain to produce dipeptides and **amino acids**. Exopeptidases are produced in the pancreas and secreted into the duodenum (Figure 56).

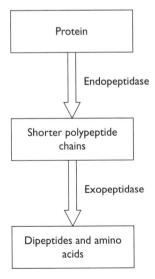

Figure 56 Summary of protein digestion

Knowledge check 33

Explain the advantage of releasing both endopeptidases and exopeptidases into the gut.

Summary

Table 15 A summary of chemical digestion of starch, proteins and lipids

	Carbohydrates		Triglycerides	Proteins	
Mouth (pH 6.5–7.5)	Starch				
	Amylase				
	Maltose				
Stomach (pH 2)				Proteins	
				Endopeptidase (e.g. rennin)	
				Polypeptides	
Duodenum (pH 7–8.5)	Starch	Maltose	Triglycerides	Proteins	Polypeptides
	Amylase*	Maltase	Lipase*	Endopeptidase* (e.g. trypsin)	Exopeptidase*
	Maltose	Glucose	Fatty acids and glycerol	Polypeptides	Amino acids

*Produced by the pancreas
Enzymes are written in red

Absorption

Absorption takes place by simple diffusion, facilitated diffusion, active transport and osmosis. It takes place in the ileum, which has several adaptations:

- A large surface area:
  - very long — about 4 m in length
  - highly folded
  - mucosa forms finger-like villi (Figure 57)
  - the epithelial cells of the villi possess microvilli
- A short diffusion pathway — the epithelium is only one cell thick
- A steep diffusion gradient. Within each villus there are:
  - **blood capillaries**, which remove glucose and amino acids, keeping their concentration low
  - **lacteals** (part of the lymphatic system), which remove fatty acids, glycerol (and monoglycerides), keeping their concentration low

Epithelium

Capillary network: sugars and amino acids pass into the blood

Lacteal: fatty acids, glycerol, and fat droplets with bile salts pass into the lymph

Arteriole   Venule

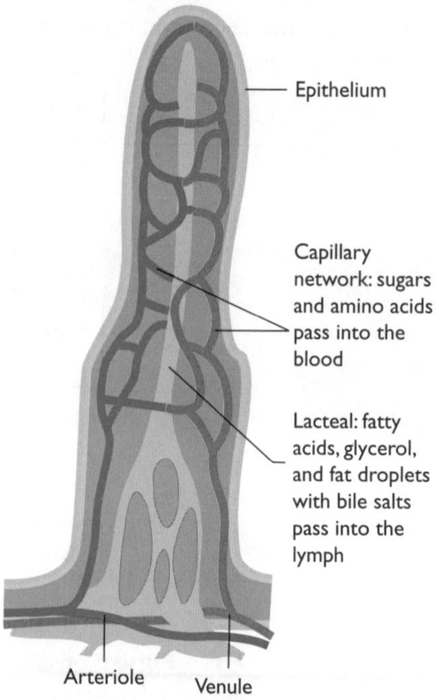

Figure 57 Cross section through a villus

Knowledge check 34

State one other function of the lymphatic system that you have studied in this unit.

Simple diffusion

Fatty acids and glycerol are both **non-polar molecules**, and diffuse through the phospholipid bilayer of the epithelial cells. They are then absorbed into the lacteals, and eventually pass into the blood via the thoracic duct.

Facilitated diffusion and active transport

Glucose and amino acids are **polar** molecules absorbed through specific **carrier proteins** in the plasma membrane of the epithelial cells (Figure 58). They are then absorbed into the blood capillaries.

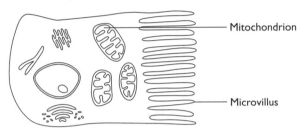

Figure 58 An epithelial cell from the ileum

The epithelial cells are adapted by having:
- **microvilli** — which provide a larger surface area for absorption
- many **mitochondria**, to produce the ATP required for active transport

Osmosis

Due to the absorption of solutes the water potential of the blood falls. This generates a **water potential gradient** causing a large volume of water to be absorbed into the blood by **osmosis**.

The large intestine (colon)

The colon absorbs the remaining water, together with vitamins (secreted by microorganisms in the colon) in order to produce solidified faeces. Residues of undigested cellulose, bacteria and sloughed cells pass along the colon to be egested as faeces. Cellulose fibre is required to provide bulk and stimulate peristalsis.

Fate of absorbed products of digestion

Fatty acids and **glycerol** are used to synthesise phospholipids for **plasma membranes** and some **hormones**. Excess fatty acids and glycerol are stored as fat in adipose tissue.

Glucose and **amino acids** travel via the hepatic portal vein to the liver. Glucose is absorbed from the blood by cells, to be used in respiration to release energy. Excess glucose is converted to **glycogen** and **lipid** for energy storage.

Amino acids are absorbed for synthesis of proteins, for example enzymes, hormones, antibodies and carrier proteins. Excess amino acids cannot be stored as the amine group is toxic, so they are **deaminated**, whereby the amine groups are removed and

Examiner tip
You are only expected to know the digestion of starch, proteins and lipids, the products formed, how these are absorbed and their fate. You have already gained much of this knowledge from Unit I, when you studied biological molecules and plasma membranes.

converted to urea. The organic acids that remain are converted to carbohydrate and either respired or stored (Figure 59).

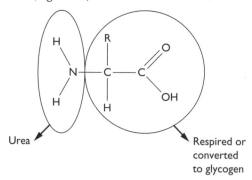

Urea

Respired or converted to glycogen

Figure 59 Excess amino acids are deaminated; in the liver the toxic amine group is removed and converted to urea and the rest is respired or converted to glycogen

Carnivores and herbivores

Different mammals have evolved different adaptations to their guts to reflect their specialised diets.

Carnivores

The gut of a carnivore is relatively short — this is due to the fact that protein is easily digested. The dentition and powerful jaw muscles of a carnivore are adapted for catching and killing prey, cutting and tearing meat and crushing bone (Figure 60). The jaw moves in a vertical plane, enabling the carnivore to open its mouth widely for catching and killing prey.

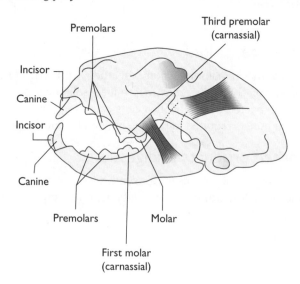

Figure 60 A carnivore skull

Table 16 How the dentition of a carnivore is adapted to its diet

Teeth	Structure	Function
Incisors	Sharp	Grip and tear flesh from the bone
Canines	Large and backward facing	Seize and kill prey
Carnassials (modified premolars and molars)	Modified premolars and molars with sharp cutting edges	Slice meat
Molars	Flattened with sharp edges	Crush bone

Herbivores

The gut of a herbivore is relatively long — this is due to the fact that plant material is difficult to digest.

The dentition of a herbivore is adapted for cutting and grinding tough plant material (Figure 61). A grazing herbivore, such as a cow or sheep, has a jaw that moves in a horizontal plane, which produces a circular grinding action. A herbivore's teeth continue to grow throughout its lifetime (as they have open, unrestricted roots).

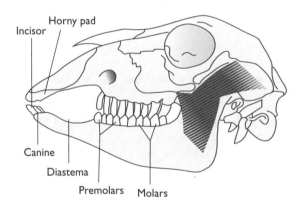

Figure 61 A herbivore skull

Table 17 How the dentition of a herbivore is adapted to its diet

Teeth	Structure	Function
Incisors	Small and flat topped — found on lower jaw only	Cut grass against a horny pad on the upper jaw
Canines	Indistinguishable from the incisors	–
Diastema	Gap that separates the front teeth from the premolars	The tongue operates in this gap to move the freshly cut grass to the back of the mouth
Premolars and molars	Large surface area, interlocking surfaces and sharp enamel ridges	Efficient for grinding plant material

Knowledge check 35

Prepare a table to compare the dentition of a fox and a sheep.

Examiner tip

Make sure you know the names of the different types of teeth and can link them to their mode of action.

Ruminants

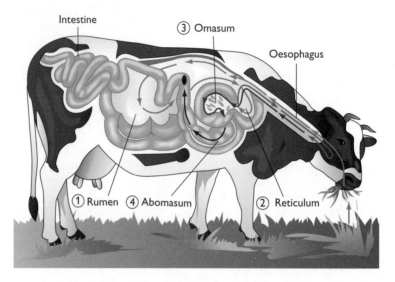

Figure 62 A ruminant with regions of the stomach labelled

Most of a herbivore's diet consists of **cellulose** cell walls. However, mammals do not produce the enzyme **cellulase** to break down the cellulose. Many herbivores have therefore evolved **mutualistic relationships** with **gut bacteria** that can digest cellulose.

Ruminants (like cows and sheep) have a **four-chambered stomach**. The **rumen** is the first chamber and contains the mutualistic bacteria. The bacteria secrete cellulase, which hydrolyses the cellulose into glucose.

Ruminants 'chew the cud', i.e. they carry out **reverse peristalsis** and bring food back into the mouth. This helps to further increase the surface area of the food but also mixes it with urea (found in their saliva). The urea provides a source of nitrogen for the bacteria so they can synthesise amino acids and proteins.

Eventually the partly digested grass and dead bacteria are passed onto the true stomach (abomasum) where protein digestion occurs. The digested food then passes to the small intestine where the soluble products of digestion are absorbed.

Other types of heterotrophic nutrition

Saprophytes/saprobionts

Saprophytes (also known as saprobionts) include **fungi** and some species of **bacteria** that feed on dead organic matter, i.e. dead organisms and animal waste (faeces and urine). They carry out **extracellular digestion**:

- They secrete enzymes onto the dead organic matter.
- These enzymes hydrolyse the bonds in the organic molecules to produce small, soluble molecules.
- These molecules are then absorbed into the organism by diffusion and active transport.

Parasites

Parasites can be classified as:

- endoparasites, which live inside the body of the host, for example the pork tapeworm (*Taenia solium*)
- ectoparasites, which live on the body of the host, for example fleas

The pork tapeworm (*Taenia solium*)

The pork tapeworm (Figure 63) is an example of an endoparasite. Humans are its primary host and pigs are its secondary host. Humans get tapeworms by eating infected, undercooked pork. The pig then becomes infected by ingesting human faeces (from untreated sewage) that contain tapeworm eggs.

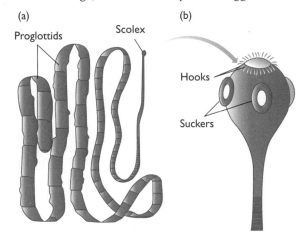

Figure 63 A pork tapeworm: (a) whole; (b) close-up of scolex

Adaptations

- Its head (scolex) has curved hooks and suckers for attachment to the gut wall.
- It has a thick cuticle and produces inhibitory substances on its body surface, which protect it from the host's immune responses and prevent its digestion by the host's enzymes.
- Its long, thin body has a large surface area-to-volume ratio for the absorption of pre-digested food by diffusion and active transport.
- It is hermaphrodite and reproduces sexually by self-fertilisation.
- Each segment contains both male and female reproductive organs and can produce large numbers of embryos/eggs.
- The eggs have a resistant shell, which enables them to survive until they are eaten by a pig.

Examiner tip

Fungi and bacteria *secrete* enzymes, they do not excrete them — excretion is removal of the waste products of cell metabolism.

A **parasite** is an organism that lives in or on another organism, its host, obtaining nourishment and causing harm to the host.

Knowledge check 37

State two ways in which infection by pork tapeworm can be prevented.

Examiner tip

The fact that tapeworms are hermaphrodite confuses some students, who make incorrect statements such as:

- 'They reproduce asexually' — they do not; they produce both male and female gametes and are capable of self-fertilisation.
- 'They produce many eggs to increase the chances of fertilisation' — this is incorrect as the eggs are already fertilised. They produce many eggs (which contain embryos) to increase the chances of reproductive success and the survival of the species.

Summary

After studying this topic you should be able to:

- define autotrophic and heterotrophic nutrition
- describe the processes of ingestion, digestion, absorption and egestion, and explain why they are necessary in animals
- describe the functions of the different layers of the mammalian gut wall
- explain why the mammalian gut is divided up into specialised regions and describe the functions of stomach, small intestine and colon
- explain how the gut of a carnivore and a herbivore is adapted to its particular diet
- compare the dentition of a carnivore and a grazing herbivore
- describe and explain the adaptations of a herbivore gut to a high-cellulose diet
- compare the gut regions of a carnivore and a ruminant (herbivore)
- describe the process of saprophytic nutrition in fungi
- explain the principles of parasitism as shown by a gut parasite such as *Taenia solium*

Questions & Answers

The unit test

When exam papers are being prepared, the examiner must try to ensure that all the topics covered in the unit are assessed, so you should prepare to get questions on any topic from Unit 2. However, BY2 is a large unit, so it would be impossible to be asked a question on everything.

Examiners must also set questions that test the specific assessment objectives (these are described in the WJEC Biology specification and also referred to in this Question and Answers section) and you may find it useful to understand the weighting of the assessment objectives that will be used.

There are 70 marks available in the BY2 exam; approximately half of the marks available target AO1 (recall of knowledge and understanding) and the other half target AO2 (application of knowledge and understanding). There will always be a few marks targeting AO3 (how science works) and these will probably relate to practical work you have carried out during the course.

The assessment objectives are weighted as follows:

Assessment objective	Brief summary	Approximate percentage of marks available	Approximate marks available
AO1	Recall of knowledge and understanding	47.5	33
AO2	Application of knowledge and understanding	47.5	33
AO3	How science works	5	4
Total		100	70

About this section

This section contains questions on each of the topics. They are written in the style of the questions in BY2, so they will give you an idea of what you will be asked to do in the exam. After each question there are answers by two different students and then examiner comments on what they have written.

Examiner's comments

Each question is followed by examiner tips on what you need to do in order to gain full marks (shown by the icon ⓔ). All student responses are then followed by examiner comments. These are preceded by the icon ⓔ and highlight where credit is due. In the weaker answers, they also point out areas for improvement, specific problems and common errors such as lack of clarity, irrelevance, misinterpretation of the question and mistaken meanings of terms.

Question I **Biodiversity and classification**

The Galapagos is a group of volcanic islands in the Pacific Ocean that were formed approximately 4 million years ago. The islands contain many endemic species (i.e. only found on the Galapagos), although they resemble similar species found on mainland Ecuador approximately 1000 km away.

(a) State what is meant by the term species. (1 mark)

The diagram below shows a simple phylogenetic tree for some of the Galapagos finches.

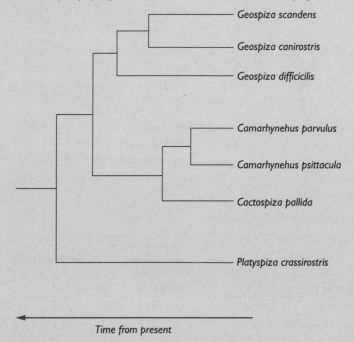

Geospiza scandens

Geospiza canirostris

Geospiza difficicilis

Camarhynehus parvulus

Camarhynehus psittacula

Cactospiza pallida

Platyspiza crassirostris

Time from present

(b) (i) To which phylum do birds belong? (1 mark)
   (ii) How many different genera are shown in the diagram. (1 mark)
   (iii) Which two species of finch are the most closely related. Give a reason for your answer. (2 marks)
   (iv) What biochemical method could have been used to determine that these two species are the most closely related? (1 mark)
   (v) Describe how this method would show that they are closely related. (1 mark)

(c) Charles Darwin suggested that the different species of finch have evolved from a common ancestor that arrived from mainland Ecuador. What is the name given to the evolutionary diversification from a single common ancestor? (1 mark)

Total: 8 marks

ⓔ Classification is commonly assessed via structured questions like this one and you must make sure that you have learnt all of the key terms in this section. Part (a) of this question is straightforward and is an easy mark for simple recall. Part (b) tests both recall with understanding (AO1) and application of knowledge and understanding (AO2); you must use the information in the diagram and read the questions carefully, otherwise it is easy to lose marks. Part (c) is only testing recall but you must make sure you read the question carefully and choose the correct term.

Student A

(a) A group of organisms that are capable of interbreeding. **a**
(b) (i) Chordates **b**
     (ii) 3 **c**
     (iii) *Camarhynchus parvulus* and *Camarhynchus psittacula* **d** as they evolved most recently **e**.
     (iv) DNA analysis **f**
     (v) That both species would have the same bases **g**
(c) Natural selection **h**

ⓔ **2/8 marks awarded a** Student A has only given half a definition and failed to state that they would produce fertile offspring. **b** Correct. **c** Incorrect; the student has looked at the groupings of the birds and not the names of the genera. **d** Correct. **e** The answer is too vague. **f, g** Again the answer is too vague — all species on Earth contain the same four bases. **h** Student A has failed to read the question carefully and has given the term for the mechanism of evolution.

Student B

(a) A group of organisms that are capable of interbreeding to produce fertile offspring. **a**
(b) (i) Chordata **b**
     (ii) 4 **c**
     (iii) *Camarhynchus parvulus* and *Camarhynchus psittacula* **d** as they have the most recent common ancestor and the most recent point of divergence **e**.
     (iv) DNA fingerprinting **f**.
     (v) It would show that the amino acid sequences would be very similar. **g**
(c) Adaptive radiation **h**

ⓔ **7/8 marks awarded a–d** All correct. **e** Good use is made of the diagram and the student has clearly linked the point of divergence with the presence of a common ancestor. **f** Correct. **g** The student has confused the different biochemical tests — DNA fingerprinting would show that the banding pattern of the two fingerprints would be similar. **h** The student has read the question carefully and has given the correct response.

ⓔ **Student A has lost some easy marks by giving an incomplete definition and vague answers regarding DNA analysis. 2 marks only are awarded (grade U). Student B, however, gains 7 marks (grade A) for simply learning some straightforward biology. It is important that you learn definitions associated with this topic as there are several that could be asked about, and it is easy to use the wrong term as Student A did in part (c).**

Question 2 Gas exchange

The diagram below shows a cross-section through an alveolus and associated blood supply in the mammalian lung.

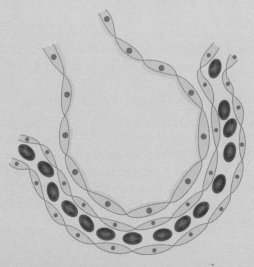

(a) (i)   Using the diagram describe two adaptations of the lungs for gas exchange.   (2 marks)
   (ii) Explain why it is necessary for mammals to ventilate their lungs.   (1 mark)

(b) Describe and explain the process of inspiration in a mammal.   (4 marks)

(c) Fish use their gills to obtain oxygen from the surrounding water. Some species of fish ventilate their gills using countercurrent flow, while others have a parallel flow system.
   (i)   What is meant by the term countercurrent flow?   (1 mark)
   (ii) Explain the advantages of countercurrent flow compared with parallel flow for a fish.   (2 marks)

Total: 10 marks

ⓔ This is a typical question on gas exchange and tests recall with understanding on different organisms (AO1). Notice that part (a)(i) requires you to use the diagram and therefore restricts the answers available. Part (b) is straightforward but take note of the mark tariff; you can easily lose marks for lack of detail and you must make sure your answer clearly links cause and effect. Part (c) tests recall (AO1), so you should find it easy.

Student A

(a)   (i) It is permeable to gases **a** and has a large surface area **b**.
      (ii) Mammals ventilate their lungs to breathe in air with a higher concentration of oxygen **c**.
(b) The intercostal muscles contract **d** expanding the ribs **e**. This causes the pressure in the lungs to fall **f**. Air moves into the lungs causing the lungs to inflate **g**.
(c)   (i) The water and the blood flow in different **h** directions in the gills.
      (ii) In countercurrent flow equilibrium is never reached **i** and therefore diffusion occurs all the time **j**.

ⓔ **3/10 marks awarded a** Student A has simply recalled a feature from memory and not used the diagram, and **b** has failed to name the feature that provides the large surface area. **c** The explanation has not made the link with maintaining concentration gradients. **d** Correct. **e** It is important to communicate answers clearly. The ribcage can expand but individual ribs cannot. **f** Correct. **g** The answer shows confusion, and the cause and effect are incorrect. **h** Again, poor terminology has prevented the student gaining the mark; different is not the same as opposite. **i** Correct. **j** This is a common error — diffusion will always be occurring in some part of the gill regardless of the mechanism. It is important to write that it occurs across the *entire length* of the gill plate.

Student B

(a)   (i) There is a film of water, so it is moist, which allows gases to dissolve. The alveolar walls are one cell thick, providing a short diffusion pathway. **a**

    (ii) To maintain steep concentration gradients between the oxygen in the alveolus and in the blood. **b**

(b) The intercostal muscles contract pulling the ribcage upwards and outwards. The diaphragm contacts and flattens. This increases the volume of the lungs, which lowers the pressure in the lungs. Air moves into the lungs down a pressure gradient. **c**

(c)   (i) In countercurrent flow mechanism the water flows over the gills in the opposite direction from the blood flow. **d**

    (ii) Countercurrent flow ensures that the concentration gradient is maintained across the entire gill plate. Therefore oxygen will diffuse into the blood along the whole length of the gill plate; the fish can therefore gain more oxygen. **e**

ⓔ **9/10 marks awarded a** This gains 2 marks because the student has clearly linked the structure with the relevant adaptation to gas exchange. **b** Correct. **c** This is a well-structured answer — the contraction of the different muscles is clearly linked to the effect on the relevant anatomical structures; cause and effect are also clearly stated, so this gains 4 marks. **d** Correct. **e** The answer demonstrates a good understanding of countercurrent flow but the question is asking for a comparison between the two mechanisms; the only comparative statement is with regard to more oxygen, so this only gains 1 mark.

ⓔ **If you are well prepared you should be able to gain most of the marks available on these types of questions. Student A has given answers that lack the detail and precise use of terminology that is expected at this level. S/he gains 3 marks (grade U). In contrast Student B gains 9 marks (grade A) for clearly linking structure to function and cause and effect. S/he has spent time learning the biology that they were taught. The instruction in part (c)(ii) to 'compare' means that you will be penalised heavily if you don't.**

Question 3 Transport of water in plants

The diagram below shows the transverse section of a root as seen using a light microscope.

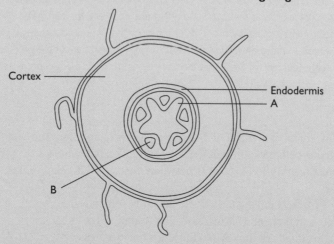

Cortex

Endodermis

A

B

(a) (i)   Name the structures labelled **A** and **B**. (1 mark)

(ii) **Explain the role of the endodermis in the uptake of water.** (3 marks)

The graph below shows the transpiration rate of a plant, measured at regular intervals over a 24-hour period.

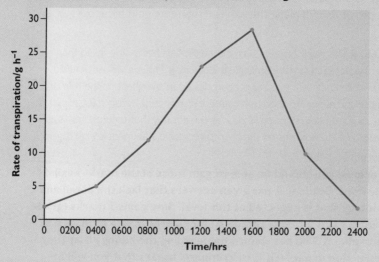

(b) (i)   **Calculate the percentage increase in rate of transpiration between 0400 hrs and 1600 hrs. Show your working.** (2 marks)

(ii) **Explain the difference in transpiration rate at 0400 hrs and at 1600 hrs.** (3 marks)

(c) **Cohesion–tension theory explains the movement of water up the stem of a plant. Use your knowledge of transpiration to explain why it is known as *cohesion–tension* theory.** (3 marks)

(d) **A potometer can be used to measure the rate of transpiration in a leafy shoot. Describe two precautions that you should take when setting up a potometer.** (2 marks)

Total: 14 marks

ⓔ Although plants are not deemed 'interesting' to students, plant transport is an important aspect of Unit 2 and allows an examiner to assess many different skills, as in the question above. Parts (a) and (c) test recall of knowledge and understanding (AO1) and you should find them easy if you are well prepared. Part (b)(i) is testing your mathematical ability and you need to be precise in reading off the data. Part (b)(ii) tests your application of knowledge and understanding (AO2) and you must link the data with your biological knowledge. Part (d) assesses your understanding of how science works (AO3), and this is a practical that you should have encountered on your course.

Student A

(a) (i) A: phloem; B: xylem **a**
   (ii) The endodermis contains a layer of wax **b** which blocks the apoplast pathway **c** and forces water into the symplast pathway **d**.
(b) (i) (28/5) × 100 = 560% **e**
   (ii) The temperature is higher at 1600 hrs and therefore the water molecules will have more kinetic energy and evaporate faster, increasing the rate of transpiration. **f** 0400 hrs is in the middle of the night **g** and therefore the plant cannot photosynthesise and therefore does not need as much water, so the rate of transpiration is lower **h**.
(c) Cohesion means that water molecules stick to one another **i** as they are pulled up the xylem **j**.
(d) You need to make sure that all the equipment is airtight **k** and that you repeat the experiment three times to calculate a mean **l**.

ⓔ **4/14 marks awarded a** Incorrect. **b** Reference to the layer of wax is vague; the cell walls contain the waxy substance suberin. **c, d** Correct. **e** The student has simply used the values from the graph in the calculation and therefore not calculated the percentage difference in rate — no marks. **f** Student A has explained one observation correctly, **g** however the second point is vague and should make reference to light intensity. **h** The final statement shows a lack of understanding. Photosynthesis can occur due to water being drawn up the stem to the leaves but it does not cause transpiration; evaporation of water from the leaves via stomata causes transpiration. **i** This is poor terminology. At AS reference must be made to hydrogen bonding or a strong attraction between water molecules. **j** This second statement is also vague. **k** Correct. **l** Repeating an experiment and calculating a mean increases the reliability of the data collected, it is not a precaution when setting up the equipment and therefore does not gain a mark.

Student B

(a) (i) A: xylem; B: phloem **a**

(ii) The endodermis contains a Casparian strip **b**, which is waterproof **c** and blocks the apoplast pathway, forcing water into the symplast pathway **d**.

(b) (i) 28 − 5 = 23

(23/5) × 100 = 460% **e**

(ii) At 1600 hrs the rate of transpiration is higher than at 0400 hrs. This can be explained because there is an increase in light intensity **f**, which increases the rate of photosynthesis **g**. As a result more ATP is available to actively transport K^+ into the guard cells **h**, lowering their water potential. Water enters the guard cells by osmosis, causing them to become turgid **i** and opening the stomata, so more water is lost from the leaf **j**.

(c) Cohesion is due to hydrogen bonding between water molecules **k**. Tension is due to the column of water being pulled up the xylem from the top **l**.

(d) The leafy shoot needs to be cut and placed in the potometer under water **m** and it should be left in the potometer for 5 minutes to allow it to equilibrate **n**.

ⓔ 13/14 marks awarded a Correct. **b–d** This is a well written answer using precise biological terminology and gaining all 3 marks. **e** 2 marks; Student B has shown his/her working (as asked), calculating the *difference* in transpiration rate and then dividing this by the original transpiration rate before multiplying by 100. **f–j** Again this is a well written answer gaining full marks. Student B has given a concise explanation of the effect of increasing light intensity on transpiration and linked this to the rate of photosynthesis and the relationship with stomatal opening. **k, l** Both correct, however Student B has only stated the meaning of *cohesion* and *tension* and has failed to explain that the evaporation of water molecules from the spongy mesophyll causes water to be drawn out from the top of the xylem, creating the tension — 1 mark lost. **m, n** Correct.

ⓔ Examiners see students achieving a broad range of marks on questions regarding plants. Most AS biology students prefer to study aspects of animal biology and focus on these topics during revision. This may well be the case for Student A as the majority of the answers are vague and lack understanding; s/he gains 4 marks (grade U). In contrast, Student B has spent time learning the biology involved and has gained 13 marks (grade A). Most of the biology associated with gas exchange and transport in plants is easier than most students imagine; you just need to take the time to learn it. This question also highlights the need to pay attention and make notes during practical lessons; the skills you are learning are assessed in the exams as well as in the practical assessment (BY3).

Question 4 The mammalian heart

The graph shows pressure changes in the left ventricle, left atrium and aorta.

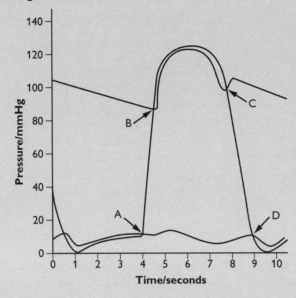

(a) (i)   Choose the appropriate letter from the graph that corresponds to each of the following.   (3 marks)

	Letter
Aortic (semi-lunar) valve opens	
Blood starts to enter the left ventricle	
Bicuspid (atrio-ventricular) valve closes	

(ii) Using the information on the diagram above, calculate the pulse rate per minute for this person. Show your working.   (1 mark)

(b) A similar graph can be produced to show the pressure changes in the right side of the heart. The trend of the graph is the same, however the maximum pressure recorded is lower than in the graph above. Explain the reason for this.   (1 mark)

The diagram below shows a vertical section through the human heart. The structures labelled X, Y and Z are associated with the cardiac impulse that brings about muscle contraction.

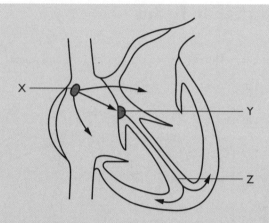

(c) Using the diagram, identify the structures labelled and describe their role during the cardiac cycle.

(5 marks)

Total: 10 marks

ⓔ Questions on the heart tend to give you a graph or a diagram to interpret, so this is typical of a question you may get in the exam. Parts (a) and (b) are testing application of knowledge and understanding (AO2). Part (a)(i) is straightforward and you should find this easy. Part (a)(ii) is not a difficult calculation and therefore is only worth 1 mark. Part (c) is testing recall of knowledge and understanding (AO1) and the diagram provided is there to help you. Notice that the names of the structures are not given on the diagram; this should be an easy 5 marks to pick up for a well-prepared student as you simply have to identify the three and state their function.

Student A

(a) (i) B a B b C c
  (ii) 60/0.85 = 70.6 d
(b) Because the right ventricle is only pumping blood to the lungs. e
(c) Structure X is the pacemaker f and generates the heart beat g. The electrical message h from the pacemaker reaches the AVN (structure Y) i and is sent down structure Z j. The message then causes the ventricles to contract from the bottom upwards k.

ⓔ **4/10 marks awarded a** Correct. **b** B is the point where blood enters the aorta not the left ventricle. **c** C is the point where the aortic valve closes. Student A may not have read the question carefully and as a result lost 2 marks. **d** Correct. **e** Although the statement is correct it has not answered the question being asked. The lower maximum pressure is due to weaker muscular contraction. **f** Correct — the sino-atrial node is also commonly referred to as the pacemaker and so this is acceptable. **g, h** This lacks the terminology required at this level — the SAN and AVN generate electrical impulses, not a message or a heart beat. **i** It is important that you give the *name* of structures; as a general rule abbreviations are not accepted by the exam board. **j** No mark, as the structure has not been identified. **k** Although the student has used the term 'message' they will not be penalised for the same mistake twice, so this final statement gains a mark.

Student B

(a) (i) B a D b A c

   (ii) 60/0.85 = 71 beats per minute d

(b) Because the wall of the right ventricle contains less muscle and therefore cannot generate as much pressure as the left ventricle e.

(c) Structure X is the sino-atrial node f and generates the cardiac impulse g. As the impulse spreads through the walls of the atria it causes atrial systole h. The impulse is then picked up by the atrio-ventricular node i and passes down the bundle of HIS j. At the base of the ventricles the impulse passes up through the walls of the ventricles causing ventricular systole k.

ⓔ **9/10 marks awarded** **a–c** Correct. **d** Correct; although the units are not required (as they are given in the stem of the question) it is always good practice to include them. **e** A correct answer clearly linking cause (thickness of muscle wall) to effect (maximum pressure generated). **f** Correct. **g, h** A concise explanation using the correct terminology. **i, j** Although the correct description has been given, the student has not linked this to the diagram and identified clearly structures Y and Z, and therefore neither point gains credit. **k** Another concise explanation using the correct terminology. Overall, Student B has written a good answer to part (c), and would have gained full marks if he/she had made reference to the diagram throughout. 4 marks out of 5 are scored — there will be at least six marking points on an exam question worth 5 marks.

ⓔ **There are only so many ways that examiners can ask questions on the heart, and the cardiac cycle graph never changes! This question is targeted at a grade E student and so high marks are expected. However, don't be complacent and think you 'know the heart', as it is easy to give answers that lack detail, as Student A has done in part (c). Student A gains 3 marks (a borderline E-grade). Student B gains 9 marks (grade A) for writing a well-structured answer. Students B's answer also demonstrates the need to read questions carefully and to do as instructed. S/he knows all of the relevant biology and should have picked up full marks, but failed to make reference to the diagram and was penalised for this.**

Question 5 **Oxygen dissociation curves**

The graph shows the dissociation curves for haemoglobin found in a lugworm and an adult human.

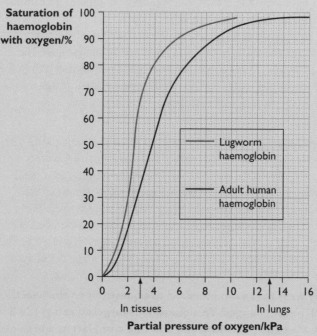

(a) How many molecules of oxygen can one molecule of haemoglobin carry when it is fully saturated?

(1 mark)

(b) For human haemoglobin, what percentage of oxygen would be unloaded to the tissues for respiration?

(1 mark)

(c) Describe how oxygen is released from the haemoglobin molecule. (4 marks)

(d) During exercise the dissociation curve for adult haemoglobin moves to the right.
 (i) What term is used to describe this? (1 mark)
 (ii) What is the significance of this effect? (2 marks)

(e) The lugworm lives in a burrow in the sand on the seashore. The haemoglobin dissociation curve for the lugworm is to the left of human haemoglobin; explain the advantage of this to the lugworm.

(3 marks)

Total: 12 marks

ⓔ This is a topic that many students find difficult. However, don't be put off by these questions as there will always be some easy marks available — for example, parts (a), (b) and (d)(i) are testing recall of knowledge and understanding (AO1) and your ability to extract data from a graph. Part (c) is also AO1 and a well-prepared student should be able to score full marks for this part. Parts (d)(ii) and (e) are testing application of knowledge and understanding (AO2). If you remember that if the curve is situated to the left then it is more efficient at loading O_2 and that if it is to the right it is more efficient at unloading O_2, you will always pick up some marks from the question.

Student A

(a) 4 **a**

(b) 65% **b**

(c) When blood flows through the lungs oxygen diffuses into the red blood cells and combines with haemoglobin to form oxyhaemoglobin **c**. As blood flows through the tissues the haemoglobin drops off the oxygen **d** and it diffuses out of the red blood cells and into the tissues **e**.

(d) (i) The Bohr effect **f**

   (ii) It allows you to keep exercising for longer. **g**

(e) As there is not much oxygen inside the burrow **h** the lugworm can still survive **i**.

ⓔ **3/12 marks awarded a** Correct. **b** Student A has been careless in reading the data from the graph and lost an easy mark. On questions like these there will always be a limited range of acceptable values and if you are careful you will always get the mark. Student A has failed to answer the question asked in part (c), either through not reading the question properly or not being fully prepared. **c** Reference to the lungs is completely irrelevant. **d** 'Drops off the oxygen' is poor terminology **e** and although the rest of the answer is written correctly, the question has not asked for this. **f** Correct. **g** This answer is too vague and lacks any biological detail relating to haemoglobin. **h** This could be written better but just about gets a mark **i** The final statement is too vague.

Student B

(a) 4 **a**

(b) 61% **b**

(c) CO_2 produced during respiration diffuses into the red blood cells and combines with H_2O to form carbonic acid **c**. The carbonic acid then splits into protons (H^+) and bicarbonate ions **d**. The protons cause the O_2 to be unloaded from the oxyhaemoglobin **e**.

(d) (i) The Bohr effect **f**

   (ii) It lowers haemoglobin's affinity for O_2 **g** and causes more O_2 to be unloaded to the muscles **h**.

(e) Having a dissociation curve to the left means that the lugworm's haemoglobin has a higher affinity for O_2 **i** and therefore can become fully saturated at a lower partial pressure of oxygen **j**.

ⓔ **9/12 marks awarded a, b** Correct. Student B has written a well-ordered answer to part (c) but it lacks some detail; they have linked the release of CO_2 with **c** the formation of carbonic acid and **d** the release of protons and **e** the subsequent dissociation of oxyhaemoglobin, and gained 3 marks. They could have made reference to carbonic anhydrase catalysing the formation of carbonic acid or the buffering of the protons by haemoglobin, to pick up the final mark. **f** Correct. **g** This is a good answer that links the position of the curve with haemoglobin's affinity for oxygen but **h** doesn't fully explain the advantage to the person exercising; during exercise there is an increased rate of respiration and therefore more O_2 is required. **i** This is a good answer that again links the position of the curve with haemoglobin's affinity for oxygen and **j** the loading of O_2; unfortunately the student hasn't linked this to the environment in which the organism lives.

e **Questions on dissociation curves are aimed at the more able students. This aspect of biology is challenging to many AS biology students. However, examiners will always ensure that some marks are available to students across the ability range. Student A gains 3 marks (grade U), as would be expected of a weaker student; however he/she could have picked up more marks by taking more care with the graph. Student B gains 9 marks (grade B) and has demonstrated some understanding of the concepts involved. Even if you struggle with dissociation curves it is important to remember that some marks are available to you. If you also remember (not necessarily understand) the following points then you will pick up more marks:**

Curve situated to the *left*	Curve situated to the *right*
The pigment has a *higher affinity* for O_2	The pigment has a *lower affinity* for O_2
Therefore it is better at *loading* O_2	Therefore it is better at *unloading* O_2
This is an advantage for any organism living in a *low-O_2* environment	This is an advantage when an organism needs *more O_2*, e.g. during exercise

Question 6 **Reproductive strategies**

The aphid *Acyrthosiphon pisum* is an insect pest of pea plants. The diagram below shows the basic life cycle of the pea aphid, *A. pisum*.

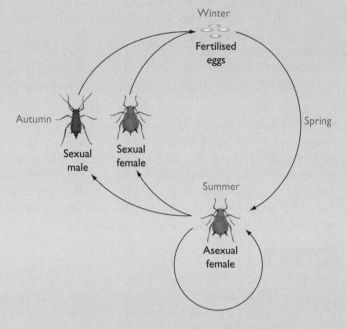

(a) (i) Explain the advantage to the pea aphid of producing only female aphids during spring and summer. (2 marks)

(ii) Describe one environmental factor that triggers the aphids to switch from reproducing asexually to sexually. (1 mark)

(iii) Explain the advantage of producing both male and female aphids in the autumn. (2 marks)

(b) Sexual reproduction occurs in many species of animal including frogs and gorillas. Explain why gorillas produce fewer gametes and have fewer offspring than frogs. (3 marks)

Total: 8 marks

ⓔ Questions on reproductive strategies tend to focus on the advantages and disadvantages of asexual or sexual reproduction. Part (a) of this question tests application of knowledge and understanding (AO2) by giving a diagram of the life cycle of an insect that can reproduce both asexually and sexually. Although it may appear difficult, it is a fairly straightforward question. Part (b) tests recall of knowledge and understanding (AO1) so a well-prepared student will easily pick up full marks. However, it is important to remember that you are being asked to compare two different animals, so you must make reference to both in your answer.

Student A

(a) (i) Asexual reproduction is quicker **a** and the females don't need to find a male to mate with **b**.

(ii) There may be overcrowding due to lots of aphids **c**.

(iii) So the males and females can reproduce sexually to produce offspring that have variation **d**. They will produce eggs that are resistant and can survive during the winter **e**.

(b) Baby gorillas are looked after by their parents and this increases their chances of survival **f** therefore gorillas don't need to have many babies. Gorillas also live in groups and the silverback will protect all the gorillas in the group **g**.

ⓔ **3/8 marks awarded a** Student A has started with a vague answer (what is it quicker than?) that is not worthy of credit. **b** However, the second statement puts the first into some context and gains a mark. **c** Correct. **d** Student A has the correct idea but the answer lacks precision and doesn't get the mark. This is a common error — it is important to write that sexual reproduction produces *genetic* variation. **e** Correct. **f** Student A has not made a comparative statement, so no mark is awarded. **g** Student A has started drawing on general knowledge rather than the biology they have been taught; this shows a lack of preparation.

Student B

(a) (i) Asexual reproduction produces clones **a**. As environmental conditions are stable during the summer there can be a rapid increase in population allowing the aphids to colonise the area **b**.

(ii) During the autumn the environmental conditions are changing and the weather is getting colder **c**.

(iii) The males and females can reproduce sexually and will produce offspring that have genetic variation **d**. This allows the offspring to adapt to the changing environment **e**.

(b) Internal fertilisation (used by gorillas) increases the chance of successful fertilisation and so gorillas produce fewer gametes than frogs, which reproduce using external fertilisation **f**. The gorilla embryo develops inside its mother's uterus and is protected from the external environment **g**. Gorillas also give a lot more parental care than frogs so the gorilla baby is more likely to survive **h**.

ⓔ **6/8 marks awarded a** Student B has given a concise statement and **b** linked it to the relevant biology, gaining both marks. **c** Correct. **d** Correct — Student B has made reference to *genetic* variation. **e** Incorrect — this is a common error. Individual offspring are unable to adapt to changing environments; genetic variation ensures that some of the offspring will survive the unfavourable conditions, allowing the *species* to adapt. **f** This comparative statement made with regard to gametes gets a mark. **g** This statement is correct but unfortunately Student B has failed to make a comparison with frogs. **h** Correct.

(e)   The topic of reproductive strategies has a limited content and focuses on four main areas:

- the advantages and disadvantages of asexual and sexual reproduction
- the reproductive strategies of vertebrates
- reproduction in insects
- reproduction in plants

This topic does not contain any complicated biology and if you are well prepared you should gain high marks on these questions. There are, however, a couple of pitfalls to avoid. One is giving answers that lack precise biological detail, which both students fell into. The other is relying too much on general knowledge and not what you have been taught, as shown by **Student A. Student A** scores 3 marks, which would be expected by an E-grade student, while **Student B** gains 6 marks (grade B). By paying a bit more attention to detail both students could have picked up more marks.

Question 7 The human digestive system

The diagram below shows the main parts of the digestive system of a human.

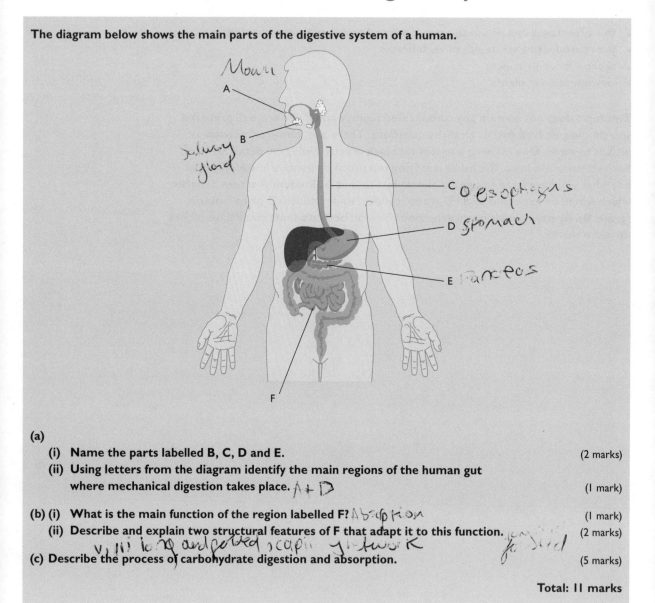

(handwritten labels on diagram)
Mouth
A
B — salivary gland
C — oesophagus
D — stomach
E — pancreas
F

(a)
   (i) **Name the parts labelled B, C, D and E.**   (2 marks)
   (ii) **Using letters from the diagram identify the main regions of the human gut where mechanical digestion takes place.** A + D   (1 mark)

(b) (i) **What is the main function of the region labelled F?** Absorption   (1 mark)
   (ii) **Describe and explain two structural features of F that adapt it to this function.** *(handwritten)*   (2 marks)
villi long and folded, capillary network

(c) Describe the process of carbohydrate digestion and absorption.   (5 marks)

Total: 11 marks

(e icon) This is a typical question on human digestion and tests mainly recall with understanding (AO1) by use of a labelled diagram, so you should find it easy. Notice that in part (a)(i) four correct labels are required to gain both marks. Part (c) is straightforward but take note of the mark tariff. You can easily lose marks for lack of detail and you must make sure your answer is written in the correct sequence.

Student A

(a) **(i)** A: mouth, B: oesophagus, C: stomach, D: pancreas **a**

(ii) A **b**

(b) **(i)** Absorption **c**

(ii) It is long and folded to form villi, which increase the surface area for absorption **d** and the epithelium is only one cell thick **e**.

(c) Starch is broken down into glucose in the mouth by salivary amylase **f**. The glucose then passes down the oesophagus and through the stomach into the small intestine where it is absorbed into the blood **g**.

ⓔ **5/11 marks awarded a** Student A has lost 1 mark for incorrectly identifying A as the mouth. **b** This is a common error — the student has only linked the mouth with mechanical digestion. **c** Correct. **d** Student A has linked the first feature with an explanation, but **e** has only stated the second feature and not linked this to a short diffusion pathway, so loses 1 mark. The answer for part (c) is poor because Student A has failed to learn some straightforward biology. 1 mark is awarded for **f** correctly identifying the enzyme involved in the digestion of starch and **g** stating that glucose is absorbed into the blood.

Student B

(a) **(i)** A: salivary glands, B: oesophagus, C: stomach, D: pancreas **a**

(ii) A and D **b**

(b) **(i)** Absorption of the products of digestion **c**

(ii) It is long and folded to form villi, which increase the surface area for absorption **d**. The villi contain a dense capillary network to remove the products of digestion, maintaining steep concentration gradients **e**.

(c) Starch is hydrolysed into maltose **f** by the enzyme amylase **g**. Digestion of starch begins in the mouth using salivary amylase produced by the salivary glands. Starch is also broken down in the small intestine by pancreatic amylase **h**. The maltose is then hydrolysed into glucose **i** in the small intestine by the enzyme maltase **j**. The glucose is then absorbed into the blood capillaries **k** by diffusion and active transport **l**.

ⓔ **11/11 marks awarded a–c** Correct. **d, e** Student B has clearly linked the structural features with an appropriate explanation. The answer for part (c) is excellent — Student B is clearly well prepared and has used the appropriate biological terminology expected at this level. **f–l** All of the points made are worthy of credit, so full marks are awarded.

ⓔ **This relatively easy question would be one of the earlier questions on an exam paper. It is aimed at E-grade students and most students would be expected to gain high marks. Part C is worth 5 marks and is an opportunity for students to demonstrate what they know. Questions that are worth 3 or more marks tend to have more marking points than marks available. In this case there would be at least 6 marking points, so you do not have to remember everything to get full marks. Student A has scored 5 marks (borderline grade D) and has given an answer to part (c) that would be expected from a GCSE student. Student B, in contrast, has gained full marks (grade A).**

Question 8 Nutrition and parasitism

State the term for the following:

(a) (i) The synthesis of complex organic molecules from simple inorganic molecules, using a
        source of energy.   (1 mark)
   (ii) Waves of muscular contraction that push food through the gut.   (1 mark)
   (iii) An organism that secretes enzymes onto dead organic matter and then absorbs
         the soluble products.   (1 mark)

The diagram below shows the pork tapeworm *Taenia solium*.

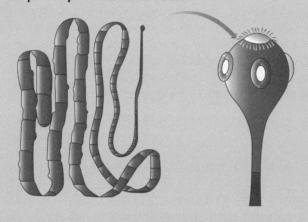

(b) Define the term parasite.   (1 mark)

(c) Using the diagram describe and explain two features of the tapeworm that show how
    the parasite is adapted to its way of life.   (2 marks)

(d) Tapeworms possess both male and female reproductive organs, i.e. they are hermaphrodites.
    Suggest a reason for this.   (1 mark)

Total: 7 marks

ⓔ The majority of this question deals with parasites. Although this topic is only a small part
of the specification, questions on parasites are common. The format of part (a) in this question
is fairly typical of the first question on an exam paper, and simply tests recall (AO1) of different
definitions. If you have learnt them this will pose no problems. Although part (b) also only tests
recall it is harder to define a term than to simply recognise a definition. Part (c) tests application of
knowledge and understanding (AO2) because you must use the information in the diagram; marks
are easily lost for simply writing features from memory. Part (d) asks you to 'suggest a reason';
the examiner assumes that you have not been specifically taught this aspect, but by using your
knowledge and the information provided you can work out the answer. It is aimed at the more
able students and tests AO2.

Student A

(a) (i) A plant **a**
       (ii) Peristalsis **b**
       (iii) A saprophyte **c**
(b) An organism that lives off a host organism, causing it harm **d**.
(c) The head has hooks and suckers **e** and it has a long thin body **f**.
(d) So that it can reproduce asexually **g**.

ⓔ **2/7 marks awarded a** Student A has given an example of an autotroph, not the name of the process. **b, c** Correct. **d** Student A loses the mark for poor terminology; parasites live in or on a host, not off a host. **e, f** Student A has stated the correct features from the diagram, but the question asks for a description and explanation, so no marks are awarded. **g** Student A has confused asexual reproduction with self-fertilisation.

Student B

(a) (i) Autotrophic nutrition **a**
       (ii) Peristalsis **b**
       (iii) A saprophyte **c**
(b) An organism that lives on or in a host organism, causing it harm **d**.
(c) The head has hooks and suckers, allowing it to attach to the intestinal wall **e**.
       It has a thick cuticle to protect it from the host's digestive enzymes **f**.
(d) The host cannot contain more than one tapeworm and therefore mating is impossible.
       Having both male and female gametes means it can fertilise its own eggs. **g**

ⓔ **6/7 marks awarded a–d** Correct. **e** Student B has selected the correct feature and explained the adaptation but in **f** the feature selected cannot be seen in the diagram and therefore does not gain credit. **g** Student B has used the information provided and his/her own knowledge to suggest a plausible explanation.

ⓔ **Although parasitism is a small topic in Unit BY2, questions about parasites have appeared in many past papers, ranging from a simple 1 mark question asking for a definition to a full structured question worth 11 marks. It is therefore important that you learn this topic well. Student A scores 2 marks (grade U) and demonstrates the importance of learning definitions. When asked to explain something, make sure you give biological reasons; Student A failed to gain any marks for part (c) because he/she failed to offer any reasons at all. Although Student B scored 6 marks (grade A), his/her answer again highlights the importance of reading the question carefully — if the question asks you to make reference to a diagram, you will be penalised if you do not.**

Knowledge check answers

1 Humans are *Homo sapiens* and the grey wolf is *Canis lupus*.
2 False. They look similar, but they are analogous structures and not homologous structures. It is important that you do not confuse the two.
3 Ground finches and tree finches are most closely related as they share the most recent common ancestor, i.e. the two groups diverged most recently.
4 In plants the cell walls are made of cellulose; in fungi the cell walls are made of chitin; in prokaryotes the cell walls are made of murein.
5 They both have segmented bodies.
6 Amphibians, reptiles, birds and mammals.
7 They are permeable to gases, thin (to provide a short diffusion pathway) and they have a large surface area. They are also moist, but this will not gain credit in questions about fish gills or other aquatic organisms! Not all gas exchange surfaces have ventilating mechanisms, or an associated blood supply (e.g. insects).
8 Ventilation maintains a steep O_2 concentration gradient between the environment and the organism, and increases the rate of gas exchange. This provides more O_2 for, and increased rate of, aerobic respiration.
9 Internal lungs help to reduce water loss from the body.
10 To maintain a constant body temperature they have high metabolic rates, as aerobic respiration releases heat energy. They therefore require large volumes of oxygen.
11 Plasma membrane; body surface/'skin'; tracheoles; lamellae; alveoli
12 This would result in excessive water loss and the plant would dehydrate; at night photosynthesis cannot occur and therefore there is no advantage to the plant if the stomatal pores remained open.
13 The movement of water and mineral ions through the xylem is passive and therefore the cells do not need to be alive. The movement of organic solutes requires active transport and therefore the cells need to be alive for this to occur.
14 Water moves through the cell walls in the apoplast pathway and through the cytoplasm and plasmodesmata in the symplast pathway. The apoplast pathway is blocked at the endodermis.
15 Any two from: a decrease in environmental temperature; an increase in humidity; a decrease in wind speed; a decrease in light intensity.
16 False. They have a thinner cuticle than mesophytes as water loss is not a problem; however, the waxy cuticle also helps to prevent the surface of the leaves becoming waterlogged.
17 If the xylem is damaged, the plant will die owing to lack of water.
18 Water is transported in the xylem in one direction — up the stem from the roots to the leaves. Sucrose is transported in the phloem both up and down the stem from 'source' to 'sink'.
19 The thicker muscle wall in the left ventricle produces higher pressure so that blood can travel further distances along the systemic circulation. Blood leaving the right ventricle only travels a short distance to the lungs and therefore does not need to be at such a high pressure.
20 They supply the cardiac muscle with blood rich in oxygen and glucose.
21 During ventricular systole all the blood leaves the ventricle, so during ventricular diastole the pressure falls to 0 kPa. However, during ventricular diastole the semi-lunar valve closes, preventing back-flow of blood into the ventricle and maintaining a relatively high pressure in the aorta.
22 The delay allows time for the ventricles to fill with blood before ventricular systole.
23 During periods of high metabolic activity, e.g. exercise or an animal escaping a predator, blood needs to be redistributed around the body. Vasodilation occurs to increase blood flow to the skeletal muscles and to the skin surface (to lose excess heat); vasoconstriction occurs to reduce blood flow to unnecessary organs, e.g. the gut.
24 Blood will flow from left to right; valve X will be closed and valve Y will be open.
25 At the venule end of the capillary the hydrostatic pressure is lower than the osmotic pressure so water moves back into the capillary by osmosis. Some of the water is not returned to the capillary and excess tissue fluid drains into blind-ended lymph capillaries and returns it to the blood via the veins of the neck.
26 Myoglobin has a high affinity for O_2 and acts as a store of O_2. It will only release its O_2 at a low pO_2, but it will release it all, which allows the muscle fibres to continue to respire aerobically (aerobic respiration is far more efficient than anaerobic respiration).
27 The hydrogen ions need to be buffered by haemoglobin and therefore they cause the oxyhaemoglobin to dissociate. This is important as it allows the released O_2 to diffuse into the body tissues for respiration.
28 Mutation
29 Internal fertilisation involves the fusion of gametes inside the female's body. The two main advantages of this are that it increases the chances of successful fertilisation and it allows the sperm (male gametes) to become independent of water.
30 Complete metamorphosis involves four distinct stages where the juveniles look different from the adults. Incomplete metamorphosis involves three distinct stages and the juveniles closely resemble the adult form.
31 Advantage: it increases the probability of successful pollination. Disadvantage: the plant must divert a lot of resources and energy into producing nectar, scents and large, colourful petals.
32 Mechanical digestion increases the overall surface area of the food that is consumed; this increases the rate of chemical digestion by enzymes, making digestion more efficient.
33 Endopeptidases produce more 'free ends' for the action of exopeptidases. This increases the efficiency of protein digestion. If only one type of enzyme was released, protein digestion would be slower and may be incomplete.
34 It drains excess tissue fluid and returns it to the blood.
35 Table comparing dentition of a fox and a sheep

Teeth	Fox	Sheep
Incisors	Sharp	Small and flat topped — found on lower jaw only
Canines	Large and backward facing	Indistinguishable from the incisors
Diastema	Absent	Present
Premolars and molars	Modified and called carnassials, with sharp, cutting edges	Interlocking with a large surface area; they also have sharp enamel ridges

36 So that the bacteria are not killed by the acidic pH found in the stomach, and are provided with the optimum pH for their enzymes.

37 By ensuring that pork is cooked thoroughly and by preventing the release of untreated sewage onto farmland.

Note: **bold** page numbers refer to definitions